OVER THE RAINBEAU

living the dream
of sustainable farming

LISA SCHWARTZ • JUDITH HAUSMAN • KAREN SABATH

RAINBEAU RIDGE PUBLISHING • BEDFORD HILLS, NEW YORK

Visit our Web site at www.rainbeauridge.com

Photos ©2009 by Karen Sabath

Design by Maura Fadden Rosenthal/Mspace

ISBN 978-0-9824427-6-0

This book was printed at Coral Graphics in Louisville, KY using vegetable-based inks on 80-pound FloMatte Text, an FSC-certified paper that contains 10% post-consumer waste fiber. It was bound at Berryville Graphics in Berryville, VA

FIRST EDITION

10 9 8 7 6 5 4 3 2 1

DEDICATED TO REDISCOVERING
THE PLEASURES IN OUR OWN BACKYARDS

CONTENTS

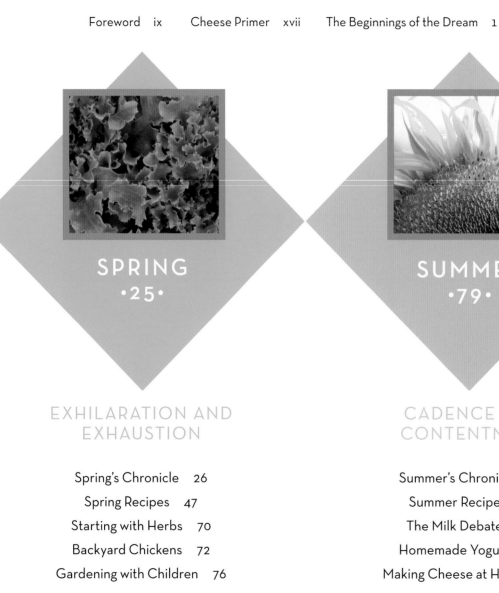

SPRING
•25•

EXHILARATION AND
EXHAUSTION

SUMMER
•79•

CADENCE AND
CONTENTMENT

FALL
•127•

WINTER
•175•

BITTERSWEET BOUNTY

RESTORATION AND
REFLECTION

FOREWORD

To me, farming is seductive. It's healthy, satisfying, spiritual and fun . . . and seductive. Imagine the morning when the dawn breaks through the pale pink and yellow clouds and lights up the apple trees. Hear the brash call of the roosters in the yard and the clucking murmur as the hens start to stir from their nests. See the soft lettuces glossed with summer dew beside the picket fence. Smell the musk of the restless bucks in their pen and the earthy mix of hay and milk in the goat barn. Run your hands over the does' flanks and their spongy teats and listen to their bellies work when you lean your head up against them while milking. You'd just have to be jazzed after that!

My farm wakes me to my surroundings like nothing else: each swelling bud of spring, the long sunsets of summer, every change in the bittersweet autumn garden and the silent poetry of the first sprinkle of snow. Rainbeau Ridge Farm creates a mojo so contagious that even my sister Karen (with her own manicured hands) eagerly picks up a chicken now and then.

But let's get this straight: I'm not a crunchy-granola-back-to-the-land-tree-hugging absolutist. I've been known to eat imported foods out of season. I farm in the suburbs, I use plastic, drive a car and wear leather. I still love to sleep late when I can. Even I have my limits on the yucky farm chores I can do. As many of us do, I live in several worlds. Sometimes it's like being "Green Acres" Eva Gabor and Eddie Albert rolled up in one person. While I love my Carharts and their farmer's daughter cachet, I don't hesitate to dress up and go black tie. Yes, I

clean up: the udders, the back ends of my does after birth, my cheese house and my kitchen.

But I also clean myself up and go to Manhattan in a suit, I was invited to speak to students at Princeton's Slow Food chapter about sustainable farming, I mix with alternative energy visionaries and I market my cheese to the chefs at top-rated restaurants.

It's not unusual for me to be running errands or making deliveries in my truck while I'm plugged into a conference call related to the philanthropic work my husband Mark and I are both involved in. I have spent time volunteering in rural schools in South Africa, packed for a fact-finding trip to the Artic and to put on a gown for a fundraiser, but truthfully, I'm always more comfortable in my jeans. In my anxiety dream, I look down and realize that under my long dress, I still have on my muck-out boots.

I didn't start out farming with a business plan or even a long term vision. I just knew I wanted to get closer to nature and my food sources and produce something of value with my own hands. With little more that a notion, moxy and a pair of milking does, I began to try my hand at making cheese. I was determined to make use of the land outside my back door and I was fortunate to have the resources to get me started. It wasn't long before my exploration evolved into something more substantial and my goals came into focus. I realized that with cheese at the core, Rainbeau Ridge could be the basis of a more sustainable life to share with my community.

Achieving sustainability takes many components: financing, environmental sensitivity, animals and staff. It became clear that I would have to diversify the farm's products and services to meet my aspirations. It would take a lot more than pulling more lettuce out of the ground or milking a few more goats to make the dream of financial sustainablility come true. I would need to add even more environmentally sustainable practices to our processes. Expanding the livestock we raised would become important to the farm's biodiversity and our educational endeavors. But diversification itself comes with a price—even working thirty-six hour days, I knew I couldn't do it alone.

I would need to carefully build out a team of staff and volunteers who shared my approach to and philosophy of sustainability.

The people who enjoy my cheese and tomatoes, the children of young families that start gardens or tap maple trees in our Sprouts, Buds and Roots programs, our teenage volunteers who line up to help in the goat barn, the poultry workshop participants that are filled with excitement about eggs, all make it clear that something is missing from their lives. With each season, I feel more deeply that Rainbeau Ridge has become a catalyst that is helping many people to fill that vacuum.

Not only for me, but for many of us, Rainbeau Ridge is a path back to the efforts and pleasures of creating real value. In a time of personless transactions and virtual experiences, we live homogenized and pasteurized lives. Our kids grow up deprived of the emotional and sensory associations between food and the way it's grown or even prepared: there are no memories in a joystick like there are in the

warmth of fresh peaches, the smell of mom's cookies or the taste of dad's tomato sauce. If I created a life of greater authenticity, you can too . . . by finding your own way in.

Understand that change may take some time. I've been at this for about seven years now and I see ever more clearly why and how skills are perfected over lifetimes. I have gained utmost respect for artisans, whether winemakers, woodworkers or shoemakers, who perfect their trade over decades. I am now able to come into the cheese house some mornings and sense a good batch just by the smell that greets me inside the door. The right hint of tangy sweetness hangs in the air, along with the maturing aroma of the week's cheese and the sanitizer that signifies the clean plant. Or, I may sense a problem brewing that day even though I'd swear I hadn't done anything differently. Like the wisdom of our grandmothers, that sensing combines art and science, a set of instincts and skills that develops step by step with experience and continues to

improve over time. The seasonal stories and photographs included in *Over the Rainbeau: Living the Dream of Sustainable Farming* are here to inspire your appreciation of rounds of cheese and yellow beets, as much as handknit sweaters, artisanal bread or u-pick berries.

Over the Rainbeau is about incremental change on our farm, but it also includes manageable One Step at a Time strategies that introduce you to interests and actions, such as making your own maple syrup, raising chickens for eggs, composting and beekeeping for honey, that can move you a little bit closer to your own goals of a more sustainable, in-touch life. And following each season, you'll find our vibrant recipes, along with those of our terrific chef-friends, created to send you off in your own inventive directions with our versatile goat cheese.

There are so many individual access points to authenticity and real food. Even city dwellers and busy people can simply gear down for a minute and talk to farmers at markets to learn about their work and the labor of love and stewardship their products represent. Then when you buy farmstead cheese, you'll understand why it can cost over twenty dollars a pound. You can change your pre-set menu ideas or grocery lists and choose to come home with a pile of turnips from the farmers market in the fall, rather than out-of-season asparagus from the supermarket, because the turnips were beautiful, bursting and alive with freshness. Your family can commit to cooking and coming together around the dinner table just one night a week. You can even grow a few cherry tomatoes and a little basil outside your window.

You can also change by buying more peaches at the height of their (brief in the Northeast!) sweet, fuzzy summer season and preserving them to taste in the winter. You can celebrate when they next come into season and savor that the winter can make us appreciate the summer peach like the dark and cold make us bask like lizards in the returning heat and light of a warm spring day.

The next time you buy those rosy local peaches, not only will the warm juice drip down your chin with each bite, not only will you close your eyes and "mmmmm" with pleasure, you will also know more about the farmer and his orchard. You will be supporting your greater neighborhood by preserving farmscape and helping to develop a new vision to revive and shape better regional food distribution with gentler environmental impact.

My life of sustainable farming and cheesemaking continues to grow like the unbridled mint in our garden, the string bean vines up the trellises, our peeping, buttercup chicks and bouncing kids and my proud stacks of snowy-white cheeses. With *Over the Rainbeau*, I invite you to join the community of Rainbeau Ridge Farm and live your part of the dream.

BEFORE YOU BEGIN

Around my house for the last few years, you don't ask, 'What goes with goat cheese?' The better question is, 'What doesn't go with goat cheese?'

As I learned to make cheese, our dinner table was the testing ground where I explored its versatility. My family may occasionally have felt like subjects in a wild culinary experiment, but in truth, my meals weren't all trial-and-error. The combinations I put before them were inspired by my belief that fresh goat cheese had a place in so many dishes. Working with seasonal ingredients, sweet or savory, winter or summer, the possible uses of goat cheese are endless.

Consider, for example, reheating leftover rosemary-roasted potatoes, drizzling them with great olive oil and dolluping with fresh goat cheese. When I improvise that way, it instantly triggers memories of the farmhouse lunches of my apprenticeship in France. Peasant food perhaps, but I call it delicious.

The idea behind the recipes in **Over the Rainbeau** is not to intimidate your culinary skills but to pique and stimulate your gastronomic imagination. Even before you take on a recipe, take a look at these seasonal pairings. Just those alone will start you imagining your own wonderful flavor combinations.

The cheeses used in the recipes reflect Rainbeau Ridge's goat cheese varieties. Unless otherwise specified, all references to "fresh goat cheese" refer to our creamy, moist Chef's Choice.

Our utmost thanks to our chef friends for their contributions to this collection, to our friends and family who endured endless tastings and to our recipe testers for their efforts.

CHEESE PRIMER

THE CORNERSTONE OF RAINBEAU RIDGE, our hand-ladled goat cheese is made fresh daily right on our farm in Bedford Hills, New York. Sometimes ash-coated, other variations include MontVivant, herb-coated, peppered, and cranberry-walnut to name a few. The immediate, short trip from milk room to cheese house is essential to the extraordinary flavor of fresh milk in Rainbeau Ridge cheeses.

Because the production is my own, I have the privilege of constant experimentation. My exploration, with new shapes and with lengthening the aging of the cheese in Camembert-like and select Gouda varieties, is promising.

The milk comes into the cheese house as warm as the goats' body temperature, just over 100 degrees, so first it must either be cooled to be stored or heated up to be pasteurized. By regulation, the milk must stay at 145 degrees for thirty minutes to pasteurize it. I watch it carefully because the whole batch will be spoiled if it reaches 160 degrees.

While the milk cools to mid-70 degrees, I choose and add the cultures that produce a certain cheese to achieve its flavor profile.

Along with the cultures, I then stir microbial rennet (not the product extracted from the stomach of a calf or young goat) into the vats of milk slowly to gently start the separation of the curds from the whey. When I return to the curds the next day, I pour off the filmy excess whey, which is fed to our chickens. I methodically ladle the chunky, prepared curds into perforated molds and arrange them so that the remaining whey drains as it should. When the curd settles in the molds, I top it off with more. After one to two days, the cheeses are drained enough to turn them out of the molds, salt them and sprinkle some with ash. Further resting or aging depends on which cheese I am making.

The cheese descriptions which follow will give you some idea of what Rainbeau Ridge cheeses are like and help you serve them, use them in cooking or make substitutions in the recipes. They follow in the venerable tradition of French goat cheeses.

CHEF'S CHOICE

These soft, unmolded curds accommodate your imagination. We flavor eight-ounce tubs of the smooth, unsalted cheese with cranberries and walnuts, sage, mixed herbs and other seasonally available ingredients. Flexible and adaptable, it's ready to combine with wherever the mood takes you: sun-dried tomatoes, figs, rosemary?

CHEVRELAIT

Our core cheese, our classic fresh chevre is made of farmstead pasteurized goat milk from hand-ladled, salted curd. It's sold in five-inch rounds (approximately eight ounces). As the name suggests, ChevreLait is the purest, most immediate capturing of the goats' milk. Its delicacy comes from its closeness to the source. ChevreLait is also moister than most fresh chevre; it is creamy, not crumbly, which may affect a cheesecake recipe, for example. It will soften as it warms but will not melt away.

While widely-available log goat cheeses, both domestic and imported, will work just fine in our recipes, many mass-produced soft goat cheeses have the goaty, sharp tang of citric acid used to accelerate the acidification process. Be sure to taste your goat cheese prior to using it in a recipe to see that its flavor will complement, not compete with, the recipe's flavors.

MERIDIAN

Organic, edible vegetable carbon ash mix adds a subtle, earthy flavor to our ChevreLait round. With the French influence, a vein of ash also transverses the five-inch round of our Meridian. This cheese celebrates a moment of contentment and accomplishment for me, the grey ash echoing my now-grey hair. The word 'meridian' itself can mean middle, but it also suggests a prime moment or crescendo. This cheese's name inspires me to keep reaching.

L'IL BLOOM

Born as a frugal way to use extra curd, the eight-ounce L'il Bloom is unashed, salted and just lightly bloomed, as its name suggests. Our customers have consistently asked for this delicate cheese with character since we first started making it. We also make this formula as ChevreLog, a convenient shape for slicing rounds.

MONTVIVANT

Shaped into the eight-ounce, traditional, truncated pyramid, similar to the French Valençay, this lightly aged, ashed and salted cheese is denser and slightly drier than the rounds. As its name suggests, MontVivant will continue to come to life with additional ripening time. It has an evolving taste and texture and will ripen in the refrigerator until a creamier layer forms just under the thicker rind, leaving the center still firm. In its round form, a nearly one-pound wheel, RondVivant extends the cheese's serving options.

OTHER GOAT CHEESE VARIETIES

The worldwide diversity of goat cheeses, represented in virtually every cheesemaking region, is amazing and tempts me constantly to try new recipes and variations. You might pick a few here to create an interesting lateral tasting platter.

GOUDA—The firmer cheese, originally in the Dutch tradition, is widely available in a goat milk version. Its flavor is nutty and its texture elastic and meltable.

FETA—Traditionally made in Greece, Bulgaria and France with a mix of sharper sheep milk and goat milk, feta is salty and crumbly.

"Artisanal" vs. "Farmstead"

Artisanal cheese is hand-crafted from milk of any type and from any source. Because it is handcrafted, it is often made in smaller quantities than commercially produced cheeses made in large facilities.

Farmstead cheese is not only handcrafted but also made from milk that is 100 percent sourced from that same farm. Because she is making cheese from her farm's own herd, the farmstead cheesemaker is in constant touch with the animals, their feed and living conditions and their milk quality. Rainbeau Ridge farmstead cheese is made daily from our goats' milk, creating the freshest cheese for which we've become known.

CROTTIN—As Charles DeGaulle said: How can anyone govern a nation that has two hundred and forty-six kinds of cheese? Even just this one has many regional, and textural and size variations. Sporting a firm rind and soft inside, this traditional French goat cheese is tangy when young and gets flakier and more intense when aged.

QUESO DE CABRA AL VINO—This is a firmer, smoother textured, wine-soaked goat cheese from Spain with a mild fruity flavor and a purple rind.

GARROTXA (/GAR-O-CHA/)—This Spanish, even Basque, goat cheese is also firmer, vegetal, and salty. It's savory and balanced.

GJETOST (/YE-TOST/)—The brown, heavily caramel-flavored, block cheese from Norway is made from goat milk.

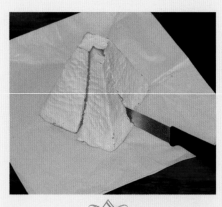

Ken Skovron of the Darien Cheese Shop showed me how to cut our MontVivant to make sure each serving has a just-right portion of rind and *pâté*. Instead of cutting from the corner, go in with your knife perpendicular to the square top and create a wedge. Then cut the wedge into smaller servings.

STORING & CUTTING

Handcrafted cheese is expensive and should be treated well to maximize its life, perfume and taste. In fact, the living yeasts and bacteria that make cheese should be coddled with proper storage. In any case, though, most of what can grow on a properly made cheese cannot hurt you. You may not like a blue bloom that appears or a slimy texture that develops, but they won't make you sick.

How long does a cheese last? For me, about forty-five minutes with a glass of wine and my favorite whole wheat crackers. But seriously, our fresh cheese will last ten days to two weeks if well-handled (Chef's Choice less because it is unsalted) and the MontVivant four to six weeks, depending on care and how ripe you like the cheese.

For storage, generally think cavelike conditions. Cheese is sensitive to changes of temperature and humidity and suffers if it dries out, when left too long on a cheese board, or is smothered with plastic wrap in the fridge. As you would with produce, buy portions you will consume in a week. Fresh cheeses especially are not meant to last long. Besides, in your more frequent trips to the cheesemonger, you will learn what's in top condition and really exciting to taste at that moment.

Try to let cheese at least lose its refrigerator chill for half an hour (some hard cheeses will benefit from an hour) before serving so its perfume can open and the texture can relax a little. Don't cut it too early. It's a good idea to supply a separate knife for each cheese on a platter to keep each flavor distinct.

Rewrap cheese in waxed paper frequently, not in plastic wrap, some say every time you cut into it. The best product is a two-layer French cheese wrap, composed of an inner, perforated plastic layer and a printed paper outer layer. The two-layered wrap allows moisture to come away from the cheese but holds it inside the outer layer. This is superior to vacuum pack (which does, however, extend shelf life tremendously).

Care in wrapping and storage is especially important with delicately flavored, nonaged cheeses such as ours. Harder cheeses, such as cheddar or Parmesan, are a little more rugged.

THE BEGINNINGS
OF THE DREAM

WHEN I TELL PEOPLE ABOUT THE FARM AND MY LIFE, some people say, "You're kidding, right?" but others say, "You're living my dream." It *is* a dream to grow quality food, make cheese, take care of my animals and influence my community. But do they understand that the dream also includes working thirteen-hour days, cracking ice from buckets in zero-degree weather, spending sleepless nights nursing newborn goats and driving around the county to hawk cheese? At this stage of life, most of my contemporaries are becoming empty nesters, retiring and taking it easy. It wasn't even my own dream of a farm that propelled me forward. The dream emerged from the work itself.

How did it happen? What kind of previous incarnation, past life experience or pivotal moment took me from a pet poodle to a few chickens and eventually to a full-fledged, diversified, organic, sustainable suburban farm? Nothing about my childhood in Poughkeepsie can explain why I liked hanging around the goat barn at the Dutchess County Fair as an adult. Or later, how my horseback riding, pet dogs and backyard chickens led to a herd of goats and life as a farmstead cheesemaker. It's a mystery even I can't fully explain.

One day when I was forty-five, I walked into my kitchen and tacked up the Nike slogan *Just Do It* above my desk. I had been imagining and researching farming for about a year. Now I was going to take that plunge or I would keep thinking of about ten dozen reasons why this wasn't a good idea and not take action. Before I knew it, I was knee-deep in goats.

Before that moment, I wouldn't have listed farming as a life-long fantasy. I was halfway through my life, wondering what I was going to do with the rest of it. I wanted to go in a new direction, not return to where I'd been. My children needed me less and less. I was hungry for hands-on involvement with something healthy for me and good for the planet. I hyperventilated just thinking about going back to school to retrain and I sure as heck wasn't going back to my first career in management consulting.

I steadied myself and took a step and then another; I put one foot in front of the other and Rainbeau Ridge took on a life of its own. The vision of its larger mission grew and new programs sprouted like the first higgledy-piggledy radish seedlings. My goats led to my award-winning farmstead cheese. Our chickens and gardens became a wait-listed Community Agriculture Partnership (CAP, our term for a variation on a CSA). My cooking classes, In Lisa's Kitchen, expanded into a year-round chef demo series. Sprouts grew Roots and Buds, our after-school and summer educational programs for children. The closed loop of sustainability strengthened as I added two cows, llamas and a small flock of rare breed sheep, brought in beehives, designed workshops and planned events.

Maybe the idea sprouted with the pet turkey I hatched from an egg purchased on eBay. Maybe it took root in my lifelong love of food and feeding others at my table or my frugal nature that hates to waste anything. Maybe the inspiration grew when we found an old architectural plat of the original farm and discovered the neglected orchard. I certainly didn't know that conserving the land we loved around our home would lead to the next phase of my life, farming a small portion of the land we eventually acquired for preservation.

The first chapter of Rainbeau Ridge opened with the neglected white elephant of a house that Mark and I fell in love with and rescued in 1988. What is now our home had been broken up into apartments and the original 150-acre country gentleman's farm around it had been sold off into suburban lots over the years. It had been over eighty years since prize-winning Guernseys grazed near the house. Our long-term goal was to reverse that tide; we committed to re-assembling as much of the original land holding as possible whenever parcels became available. We knew we wanted to restore and protect that beautiful land.

JAPANESE LESSONS

With house renovations ongoing, in 1997 Mark took a position to run the Japan offices of a large investment bank. We packed up and left the house in the capable hands of my sister Karen and her family and of our couldn't-live-without-him caretaker Kevin Ferris. That family adventure, those four years away from my "real life," sparked an urge to look for a path to something authentic. In Japan I had time to travel, absorbing language and culture, since I was taking care of a much smaller house and my kids were in school all day. I lived the floating life, observing as an outsider, exploring and learning. Almost without knowing it, I was also searching for the title of my life's next chapter.

The Japanese respect for the seasons had influences on me that would transform my life profoundly. As the season turned, women changed the dishes they used, the decorative scrolls in their homes and the school uniforms their children wore. When produce came into the markets, each arrival was celebrated by eating that fruit or vegetable as much as possible in every combination. In the States, we would wonder if a hostess had come under the influence of the latest food fad if she served tomatoes in every course, but in Japan, whether the new season meant bamboo shoots, fiddleheads or Asian pears, that prized ingredient would be served in nearly obsessive variety.

To know more about Japanese life, I took cooking courses and learned what to do with the lotus root, shiso leaf and kabocha squash I couldn't resist buying in the marketplaces and supermarkets. I ate the freshest toro off a square of paper at my favorite fishmongers' stalls and watched the 5 a.m. mayhem of brokers at Tokyo's Tsukiji fish market. I made friends with our neighborhood tofu seller. I haunted Kappabashi, the housewares district, for the best rice cooker and a tabletop hibachi. I loved the respectful ritual around food expressed in attentive displays of seasonal shape, texture and color.

In the countryside, I saw the rice paddies and bamboo shoots growing as my own awareness did. I began to feel the power of the voyage our food takes from planted seed to our dinner table. The joy of the first rice harvest, the gift of soba noodles, the care women took in arranging

five contrasting small dishes on a lacquer placemat: all of that honored the combined work that brought our food to us. An appreciation of that work was dawning on me in life-changing ways.

My own family all learned and repeated the expressions of gratitude, "Etadakimasu!" which marks the beginning of a Japanese meal, and "Gochiso sama deshita!" that marks the end. This version of (non-religious) grace-saying directed us to be aware, present and thankful for all that fed us.

Even so, at the end of our four-year stay, I missed the landscape of our Bedford home: our woods, wetlands and gardens. Upon our return to the States, I discovered that changes in sustainable farming and food models were in the air here. In Japan, I had been impressed with seasonal eating and the artistry of food. Happily for me, I had been living and feeling the very trends that were emerging at home. I had been oblivious to the development of Slow Food, the growing influence of chefs or the mainstreaming of organic farming but as I began to investigate these movements and turn towards farming, I met wonderful people. I also saw I didn't have to go back to school or be an expert to start taking steps. I could jump in and make connections through food and the farm, widening the circle by learning, sharing and *Just Doing It.*

When my children were small, the two dozen Rhode Island Red pullets we kept fertilized our small vegetable garden and the garden scraps fed the chickens that gave us eggs. Already then, I was awed by what a backyard can yield with a little care and tending. That first year back, I wanted to go further. I saw I could bring the farm back to the land; I could put it to work. My stewardship would be to nurture and cultivate the land and the land would give back. That way I could get my hands dirty and I could act, not pontificate. I was falling in love with the idea of creating something real and tangible with my own two hands, unlike an analytical piece from my consulting days or an event from my charity fundraising experiences. Goats and cheesemaking seemed a manageable challenge and farming sustainably would be the intersection of all those feelings and motivations.

GETTING MY GOATS

In the summer of our return, my family went to the Dutchess County Fair as Mark and I had always done, even as high school sweethearts. No rides or milkshakes this time though; I was there to look at goats. The reading I was doing counseled me to consider udder capacity, milk composition and quality, appearance, personality and availability. I stalked the 4-H'ers to ask them about the different breeds.

Cheesemakers recommended the all-white Sanaans for the richness of their milk. I found them monotonous; how could you tell them apart? Other breeders insisted on floppy-eared Nubians or La Manchas (even weirder with no ears!) because of their milk quality and capacity. But I just kept coming back to the multi-colored Alpines. Their markings are

endless combinations of belts, spots and blazes in beige, black, cream, white and brown. Their capacious udders would give me lots of milk from a small herd and everything I had read described the Alpines as smart, curious and beautifully diverse.

To be sure I'd take the right goat by the horns, I drove out to see the Alpines in action on a large-scale goat cheese operation also in nearby Dutchess County. There, I saw the Alpine kids' adorable leap, a little happy step that has them airborne, joy in every step, and I knew I'd base my herd on that breed. I could almost imagine them on my farm, nibbling feed from my hand while I stroked their sleek sides. I was already so smitten by them that in the end, I followed my gut reaction. After all, I'd be spending a lot of time with these animals. With care and breeding, I would build the strongest possible herd.

Now that I had settled on the Alpines, where was I supposed to get them? Suburban Northern Westchester is not exactly the dairy goat capital of the world. I had trusted my instinct up until then so I wanted to pick them out in person, to observe them in their own environment, not ship them in, sight unseen, from across the country. I had to have does that had given birth and were in milk, not kids, because I wanted to start making cheese right away. Back then, I wondered why farmers wouldn't sell me one of their two-year old does in milk. Now I know. What cheesemaker would want to sell a good doe entering the prime of her production?

I scoured the internet, contacted the American Dairy Goat Association for leads on area goat farms and, over the phone, begged goat owners to sell me two does. Eventually I convinced Carol Bunnell, a goat farmer outside of Elmira, New York who had been in the business for twenty years, to part with two dairy goats. Before she could change her mind, Ron Brooks (eventually my dependable livestock manager), Kevin and I climbed into his van to pick them up. The four-hour drive was plenty of time for self-doubt to assert itself. Anxiously, I questioned whether I would be any good at this. What was I really getting myself into? By the time I arrived, I was in a sweat despite the 40-degree weather.

The small house on a parcel of open land was the center of a bare-bones farm. The barn behind it looked like the roof might leak but

Carol's house was country-homey, decorated with her quilts and goat bric-a-brac. In her mid-fifties and dressed in a flannel shirt over jeans, she took my untrained hand in her chapped one to welcome me but we had to get down to the business of her herd. She had waited for my arrival to milk her does that morning and they were getting restless.

As we crossed the hoof-printed yard to the barn, she was already answering the many questions I was asking. The milking stanchions were worn but clean and Carol called the does according to their trained order, steadily pushing them into place with sturdy forearms for my first milking lesson.

After she demonstrated her technique with several goats, she sized me up and barked, "Sit down." I reached for the udder, grabbed the teats and squeezed: no milk. I adjusted my grip, took a calming breath and watched Carol again. I couldn't figure out why no milk emerged from the engorged, pink goat udder in my hands. Carol laughed and coached

me briskly; still nothing. I wasn't laughing. How could I have thought I could do this on my own when I returned home? My manicured nails that I had tried to hide from Carol were digging into my palms, the sweat was dripping down my back and the goat was losing patience in the stanchion, looking for relief. Finally I found the right grip and after a first quick spurt from the udder, milk began to fill the pail.

With a little more practice, I got the knack. Equipped with Carol's generous advice, Ron and I loaded the two does into Kevin's van and headed for our eight-by-twelve, home-built, starter barn. Five hours later, when I had closed the paddock gate on the goats, I reminded myself that my milking skills were passable, that I had a load of hay and grain in the garage and that I was the proud, scared owner of two beautiful, brown-eyed milking goats, Millie and Faith.

GOAT GIRL

Never an early riser, I had taken on the daily 5:30 a.m. obligation to haul myself up and out of a cozy bed to take care of the girls' morning needs. Wet, freezing, sore or exhausted, I had to be there. They couldn't wait for me to exercise or have coffee with a friend. These weren't cats, dogs or gerbils. I knew from my own early attempts that I couldn't just ask an untrained friend to sub for me.

But there were unexpected discoveries in my first spring, such as waking up to the aliveness of this time of day. No background noise from commuter traffic, school busses or trucks obscured the chattering birds. Canada geese squawked overhead as they moved to the next pond and a pair of mallard ducks returned from their winter homes. The suburban coyotes yipped their messages back and forth. The goats rustled and bleated in the barn as they moved towards the door, expecting me. I discovered that the spring dew actually has its own delicate smell. A lovely moon sometimes lingered in the sky after dawn.

The trip back to the barn for evening milking had gifts too: a chorus of spring peepers, the moment when the setting sun kisses the tops of the turning trees, then the quiet and calm and the soothing click

of the barn door closing. I learned to tell time by the sun as the days lengthened and then shortened. In March the sun lit up the big maple at 10 a.m. but by May, it was over the fenced garden at that hour. As the hues of green changed from pale chartreuse to nearly blue-green, I was moving to the cycles and senses of nature as I cared for the goats and they gave me their milk. I was committed to and hooked by the life of my animals.

My own kids were on the verge of leaving home but now my does were my kids to care for and my feelings about my cornerstone animals were intensely maternal too. When I had gone to Carol's to buy Millie and Faith, I had prepared a textbook checklist. Were their udders sturdy, their top lines straight, their legs strong-looking? I acted as if I were an expert already. In the end I chose them based on my maternal feeling.

When I needed another goat in that first season, I turned to Dot Hempler of the Triple H Ranch in Hudson, New York to replace her. By then, I was already able to ask more knowledgeable questions. What was that doe's production and kidding history? Did that tall one with the large udder have a difficult personality and was her imbalanced udder a sign of mastitis? Eventually, great conformation or not, I gravitated towards one goat in particular, named "Jewel, like the singer," said Dot. Jewel would be the companion for Faith (Hill). Somehow her name was the perfect sign I needed.

I would learn to have a lot of faith as I started up a farm with practically no experience and my girls were jewels to me. Their names also followed the goat farmers' tradition of picking a naming theme to keep track of a herd. Mine would be named after singers of all genres. For me it wouldn't be alphabetical order or flowers; I'd raise Celine, Fiona, Ella, Alanis, Etta, Norah and Blondie instead.

Without a sire for my herd, I had to return Faith and Jewel to Elmira in the fall to breed them with one of Carol's bucks. In the spring, in preparation for their first deliveries, I returned myself to knowledgeable and hearty Dot to apprentice for a week of twelve-hour days. In her cobwebbed, red barn, Dot showed me how to give shots, pasteurize colostrum, detect signs of impending labor and feed weak kids. My end of the bargain was to carry buckets of feed, clean pens and wait in the bone-chilling cold for perfect, wet triplets to emerge—nose and front hooves first—from one black-flanked doe. I could barely manage to hook closed the chained gates because my hands were so stiff in the raw cold. Every night when I drove the two hours home, I had never wanted a hot bath so badly. While awaiting my own first kids, I couldn't resist bringing home three newborns from Dot's farm: Carly, Ashanti and Macy.

ACHIEVING CHEVRE

While I needed to learn about keeping goats, I also had worlds to learn about cheesemaking. That education had begun about a month before

when I drove into the rolling hills of Massachusetts' Pioneer Valley for a day-long session with a dozen other cheese-heads walking through the basics of milk properties and cheesemaking chemistry. Ricki Carroll of Ashfield, Massachusetts was our tutor. Ricki is the wild-haired earth mother who has launched the careers of many artisan cheesemakers. She more or less wrote the book on point-and-shoot, kitchen counter cheesemaking even though she does not sell cheese herself.

We cheesemaker wannabees watched the creamy, yellow-white cow milk flow into each of our five-gallon pots and subtly change as the cheese cultures acidified the milk and the enzyme rennet coagulated the milk solids into curd, separating the yellowy whey. The sweet grass and newborn baby smells rising from the pots drew me into fantasies of early mornings in my own cheese house and of showing off my own beautiful farmstead products. I closed my eyes to lock in those aromas as reference points for the future. These sensuous, almost atavistic, cues meant more to me than the chemistry Ricki was telling us about.

Giddy with the possibilities, I kept steering the conversation back to goats and goat milk. Ricki's array of cheeses at lunchtime raised more questions about equipment, temperatures, cheese styles, timing and more. Before I left, I bought everything from her back room that I'd need to start experimenting, including the cultures she had formulated. I couldn't wait to *Just Do It.*

Ricki's workshop was a heady preview and as soon as I started milking Faith and Millie, I also began daily cheesemaking experimentation. Around my house, "What's for dinner?" became code for "Where's the goat cheese?" In the lasagna, the pizza and the cheesecake but also hidden in the chocolate pudding and the chocolate truffles, was the answer. My kids, Bari and Dan, came to the table suspicious.

At the same time, I was remembering the lessons that my family had learned with our first chickens. To expand from experimenting with milk, I wanted to build the closed loop that a diversified farm depends on: livestock that builds soil, soil that yields produce, all on a balanced scale. To accomplish that, I needed to add years of experience overnight. I had the motivation and the concept but I needed how-to expertise. When I discussed with people what I wanted to do, they all said, "You have to meet Annie Farrell."

Annie is a legendary, human Rolodex of small farming information and contacts in the Lower Hudson Valley. She was key in establishing the Agricultural District in Westchester, facilitating the County's purchase of an historic farm and in bringing to life a number of suburban farms. I was intimidated to approach her but happily, we both showed up at a mutual friend's dinner party one night. We began talking. Lucky for me, Annie was ending a ten-year commitment to another farm and we hit it off right away. I was already engaged with the goats, cheesemaking and chickens. Annie came on the following January and for about three years, helped me design, establish and expand the produce gardens of our sustainable farm, and to develop my information network and the farm's public face.

With Annie's help, we established CAP and a small ABC vegetable garden for children. Under my sister Karen's leadership, this developed into Sprouts, our after-school farm education program.

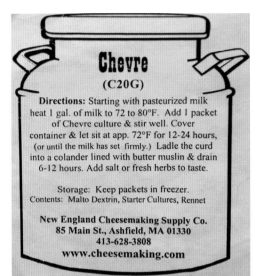

Chevre
(C20G)

Directions: Starting with pasteurized milk heat 1 gal. of milk to 72 to 80°F. Add 1 packet of Chevre culture & stir well. Cover container & let sit at app. 72°F for 12-24 hours, (or until the milk has set firmly.) Ladle the curd into a colander lined with butter muslin & drain 6-12 hours. Add salt or fresh herbs to taste.

Storage: Keep packets in freezer.
Contents: Malto Dextrin, Starter Cultures, Rennet

New England Cheesemaking Supply Co.
85 Main St., Ashfield, MA 01330
413-628-3808
www.cheesemaking.com

When we met at that dinner party, I was looking for the right next spot. I love bringing people together and Lisa needed both on-the-ground help and connections. I provided information on dairy equipment, regulations, databases, and ways to create an identity for herself and branding for her farm's products. She also needed tools, such as I had developed, to plot the farm's financial sustainability, including the garden map, the plan for the planting cycles and the per square foot, per crop, per week value program I had created.

Lisa had a timely idea because people were looking for more local food and we were establishing the Agricultural District in Westchester, which facilitates small farming. By character, Lisa is driven, blunt and urgent and she had the property, chutzpah and energy as well to make it happen. I'll never forget seeing her bulldoze the garden herself with just her son's help. She wanted to be efficient and not waste time or money. That's my nature too; I'm not frivolous. What you see is what you get with me. We both expect excellence. We work at the same Type Triple-A pace. Lisa and I were two Alpha females so at first we sometimes butted heads but as soon as we trusted one another, we sailed.

—Annie Farrell

FRENCH LESSONS

Through Annie as well, I contacted the French organization, *Alliance Pastorale*, to arrange a cheesemaking apprenticeship because I had decided to focus on what I considered classic French-style goat cheeses. I didn't worry about the language barrier; I dusted off my smattering of high school French and headed for two weeks on the Johanneau farm in Poumoue, a tiny village in Southcentral France with more goats than people.

The two and a half hour train ride from Paris sped me through the farming landscape of open fields and villages with charming squares. The Johanneau farm was made up of a rough stone house, an ivy-covered hut where the poor buck was always chained to the wall (to keep him away from the does), several serviceable aluminum sheds and a flock of red and black chickens pecking around the carved troughs in the yard. A stone-lined lane led to a barn and Monsieur Johanneau's parents' home.

During our time together, we relied on my hostess Sylvianne's little bit of English, my even littler French, and a lot of show and tell sign language. Pleasant, late middle-aged and brunette, she made their cheeses, Valençay, St. Maure and her own creation, Poumoue. She also cooked in the sparse kitchen for her farmstead restaurant on weekends.

Her short, stout husband Yves chuckled that I had come all the way to France to apprentice for just two goats. The couple had trained a dozen people to deal with large herds and considered even three hundred goats a small herd. Yves milked one hundred-fifty Saanen goats in an elegantly simple set up. With one flick of the stanchion fastener, he moved twenty does out and twenty more leaped into position. As I fell into the couples' work rhythm, I understood the efficiency and pragmatism they needed to run the farm as a business even though I would develop a somewhat different strategy.

We were out to milk by 6 and done by 8 a.m. We lugged the milk in cans to the cheese house where Sylvianne took over. The milk would not be pasteurized as French laws allow raw milk for even fresh, non-aged cheeses. Sylvianne delicately ashed yesterday's drained cheeses on

a wooden board. Then as she explained the higher butterfat of morning milk versus evening milk, she lined up exactly the right number of molds for the amount of milk she had to ladle. By noon, she had hand-ladled all the curds into molds, allowing us to retrace our steps back up the lane, picking mache and dandelion greens for a farmstead lunch.

Cheese (and of course, wine) was part of every meal, which she assembled seamlessly from the season's and region's produce. Her easy artistry reinforced the lessons I had learned in Japan about fresh, beautiful meals. She tucked a small *crottin* of their cheese into puff pastry and layered sweet, pungent St. Maure into a gratin of apple and onion or potato and leek. For our first lunch, we finished with a simple pear tart. Sylvianne used what was at hand instinctually and used every scrap; only the really inedible went into a bucket for their chickens.

Between 5 and 6 p.m. we repeated the process and set the evening milk. Then we ate again around 9:00 and sat around the comfortable wooden farm table, trying to talk politics. Imagine trying to explain in French how Americans had elected George Bush!

My notebook from those weeks is packed with sketches of barn layouts and sink arrangements, lists of equipment, scribbled notes on animal and vegetable rennet, on alternatives for culturing, a possible schedule for myself at home and the steps of each process, clarified with arrows, asterisks and labels. Even though I listened intently to the information Sylvianne offered and recorded her recipes religiously, the one piece of advice I obviously didn't follow was never be both the herdsman and the cheesemaker.

By the time I returned to Rainbeau Ridge, Jewel and Faith's kiddings were fast approaching and I was a wreck. I had focused on taking care of just them for a year but soon I would have the kids to care for too. And would my brief apprenticeship and book learning really prepare me for what would follow?

I went into round-the-clock monitoring. I had some hints from Dot but the textbooks I studied dutifully were clinical, with a long list of "signs" that does are getting ready to give birth. Their udders "bag up," their disposition changes, a ligament in their haunches softens but until I lived through those changes for myself, how could I know

Mix packet (cultures)

? proportionally
① 1 unit : 20 gal.

② Warm milk/ culture leaver
       45 minutes
    Add: 2.1 from liq. cult
         1.8 same from dry
(Comm. Women's Culturing Alliance)

(sinks - half barrel)

③ Add rennet
   { same goat / cow
   { sheep -- used 4 starter
                by ½

don't give up uniqueness
by using DVI

Ⓐ Calf - long keeping cheese
   - downside - non-veg...

Ⓑ Microbial rennets
        Cheap
  most gen. engineered

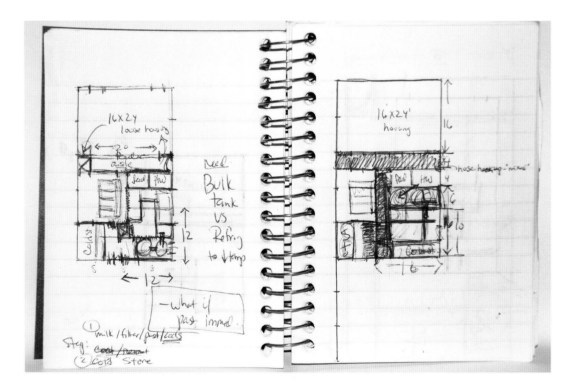

16×24
loose housing

Badar
aisle

feed HW

Cold st

12

8   3
← 12 →

Need
Bulk
tank
vs
Refrig
to ↓ temp

- what if
past immed.

① milk / filter / past / cools
Step: cool / pasteurize
② Cold Store

16'×24'
housing

16

hose housing "mixer"

Padl HW

16

16
← 16 →

what all that meant? You have to know your animals, they cautioned, but we'd barely been introduced. It seemed that my constant checking and pacing drove the does nuts too; they were like a watched pot that wanted to be left alone.

Then, one day I saw that Faith was pacing, pawing at the straw, nipping and twitching her tail, all symptoms right out of the textbook description of labor. I panicked. I couldn't ask her how long those symptoms had been going on. Would twins arrive a smooth half-hour apart, or would my doe have to labor for hours to bear a second or third kid? I prayed that I would have the strength to get through this and figure out what to do. Faith's active labor lasted about one hour (the normal range of labor is one to twenty-four hours) and the two kids were born routinely about twenty minutes apart. Within fifteen minutes, Faith had licked off the birth sacs, expelled their placenta and the kids were up and nursing. She'd done it all so smoothly and thrived…and so had I!

SPRING

EXHILARATION AND EXHAUSTION

I took a deep breath, planted my feet and placed my left hand on Ashanti's shoulder and began to blindly feel around inside the laboring doe. Her first kid had come normally, snout first resting on two little front hooves, eyes up, but nearing midnight, her labor had stopped cold. I grappled and searched for half an hour, afraid that I had lost the kid. Should I let nature take its course? I groped at a tangle of feet, and then moving up from one hoof, I felt my way up to the shoulder and finally to the neck. Without her contractions to help, I needed to be sure I had the right parts in my grip before I tugged.

Another cleansing breath, a determined, steady pull and the kid was out, and alive! I dropped to the ground, cursing, crying and then finally, laughing. Before I knew it, Ashanti's contractions resumed and she delivered a third all by herself. Thrilled and exhausted as I was with the drama I had taken part in, part of the high was succeeding as a skilled midwife, and to top it all off, that third kid was a doeling!

FOR ME, SPRING TAKES SHAPE with the does' widening sides. Just after winter's worst has passed and the first kid arrives, I get on the proverbial treadmill with no off button, moving constantly between birthing, washing, milking, pasteurizing, ladling, wrapping and back to washing and birthing again.

My hands will be raw, my back will ache, the dark circles under my eyes will be nearly permanent. On my knees deep in the muck again, I'll be worried about my girls and caught up, overwhelmed and awed. With each birth, I feel the privilege of assisting another slippery sac of

new life to slide into the world. I'll be sleeping little between attending middle-of-the-night labors, milking the full-uddered mothers and feeding them and their new kids. These responsibilities are not optional; the health and survival of the goats hang in the balance. Like sap in our maple trees, hopes for the new season rise inside me and the excitement about what's to come is as sweet as the syrup we make from that sap.

In a sense, spring begins on the farm when the days start to lengthen just a little bit in late February. To me, these one or two extra minutes of light each day beckon at the far end of the freezing tunnel of winter. There's a sweet smell of spring rain in the air and the occasional welcome break of a teasingly warm day, which move me to dog-ear those opulent seed catalogues and start choosing this year's varieties. As soon as the skunk cabbages thrust their veiny heads out of our gray wetlands, I itch to throw open the barn to air it out, to shovel out old bedding and to let in some sun.

Getting ready for the rising tide of new babies, milking and cheesemaking requires a thorough cleaning of everything. I inventory my equipment, check on supplies and make lists, lists, lists. We scrub and sterilize our cheese house walls, floors and equipment so that they are spanking clean and pass muster with our inspector in time for the official launch of our new season on April 1. I count on Kevin to tune up all the farm equipment and be sure we have plenty of hot water.

Interns and new staff arrive in early spring and must be acclimated and trained not only to be useful during the crunch, but also so they will learn as much as I promised them. Too soon, we won't even have time to assemble in the same place for staff meetings. People use the term "24/7" but they have no idea how literal that is for us all in the spring.

The hens are already laying heavily so I take the incubator out of mothballs to clean as well and set it up so we'll be ready to help hatch some chicks. In our Sprouts after-school classes, the children are fascinated by the spectacle and no matter how many times I see the patient pecking and the scrawny, wet chicks breaking out, I'm riveted too. So quickly the bedraggled chicks become fuzzy puffballs and then a few weeks later, they add their bright yellow to the yard.

Color also returns with the migrating robins, jays and finches, as well as with our splendid peacock in full courting show, which is nothing short of a masterpiece. Every time I look, his bright turquoise and chartreuse fan is more resplendent than I remember. Even the trees pitch in with their almost-glowing pink and yellow halo of leaf and flower buds. Our bees take up their part by pollinating and producing our glistening gold honey.

With longer days, the garden starts to take on more color at an accelerating pace as well. Isaac supervises the racks of tiny seedlings that bathe in blue grow lights in the office. Some crowd next to the farmhouse's big windows, waiting for the earth to warm up enough to receive them. For now, we gather nosegays of rainbow chard that have wintered over in the protection of the hoop houses. Mache, spinach and arugula planted late last fall poke though the mulch blanket as well, promising a salad soon. By the end of March, we've worked rich brown compost into the

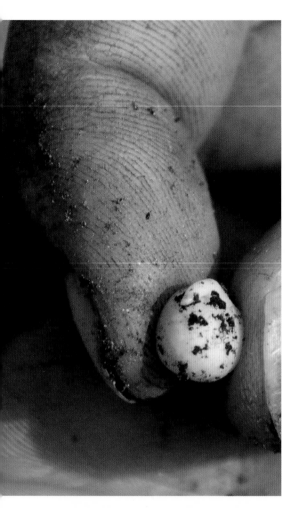

garden soil to renew it and the ten hoop house beds are a mosaic of red and green early greens and lettuces. As is tradition, we've planted the peas by St. Patrick's Day. I can almost see the tender pea blossoms that will push up along the garden fences and taste the sweet, crispy pods they'll grow into. In a week or two, CAP members will be stopping by for their first purchases of vegetables and cheese. That means the first salad with the first cheese is just days away and I can't wait.

Each member of our team at Rainbeau Ridge is specialized but in the long term, their contributions go beyond their job descriptions. The soul of Rainbeau Ridge is their involvement, their willingness to tune in and notice what the farm needs. While Kevin is fixing a tractor or involved in some other chore, he keeps an ear tuned for the sounds that signal that a laboring doe needs my help. This past year he was the one who noticed the impending birth of our Jacob lambs. To be part of it, he stayed on well beyond quitting time, late into a rainy night. He also delivers cheese at the prestigious Culinary Institute of America on his way home. Ron checks on the bucks in the morning, while in the afternoon, he might alert me to a broody hen in the hen house. In turn, as I make the weekly garden tour with garden manager (and growing genius) Isaac Jahns, he might remind me that today he's pulling the bolted arugula, which will now make a fine salad for the chickens.

Our interns also get this broad-based exposure and opportunity to learn outside their main interests and responsibilities. In 2009, garden intern Martha Hoffman learns agricultural education alongside our experienced teachers and our livestock intern Kelly Hatton apprentices in the cheese house too.

Volunteers like Aimeé Whitman and Melinda Walsh also supply committed, much-needed extra hands to the farm—and we depend on them. When Aimeé brings over her eight-year old granddaughter Georgia after school and shows her how to hold the feeding bottles just right, she shares her own childhood memories growing up on a farm and encourages Georgia's dutiful and comfortable style with the animals. On one Saturday, they even watched together as Renee gave birth.

My key retail customers are calling to ask about that first cheese too. The pressure to deliver is on, but I'm revved up by my fans' enthusiastic impatience. "Where is the cheese? I need eighteen pieces tomorrow," says cheesemonger Ken Skovron. When I finally walk into Joe DiMauro's fish store with his first order, the whole staff cheers and raises their arms in a victory salute. We high-five in front of the big sign announcing the first arrival of this year's Rainbeau Ridge cheese. Smiling like a breathless Oscar winner, I want to go on and on thanking everyone who made the cheese possible.

The 24/7 crescendo of activity in fact means no breaks and no days off for me and my team. I grab sleep when I can, maybe right after dinner, so I can be up to check the barn at midnight. I might be coddling a weak kid at 2 a.m. and later wrapping new cheese for a delivery rather than eating lunch. I'm calling potential customers, answering staff and interns' questions and on the move all day, multitasking on a pumping wave of adrenaline and gratification. I live in a frenzy of constant motion in the spring and my mind is spinning with the details.

While milking in the early morning, I'm scheming about the next cheeses I'll try with this year's increased milk production. As I arrange to sell off the first round of bucklings, I daydream with mixed emotion about supplying a meat goat operation a friend is starting. I'll also have lambs to find homes for this year and I can't be sure, but one cow might be pregnant too. I'm hoping the timing will work out so that a new round of Sprouts participants will see a perfect kid or two being born. I'm trying to get the extra hands of volunteers assigned to the most needed places. Ron, Karen and I are readying for our public event just two weeks from now, when we'll bring more people to the farm to watch our rare breed sheep being sheared. We'll use the wool for fiber-based activities with the children, and this winter I'll spin and weave some of it too. At times, it's hard to imagine what life was like before the bustle of spring on the farm.

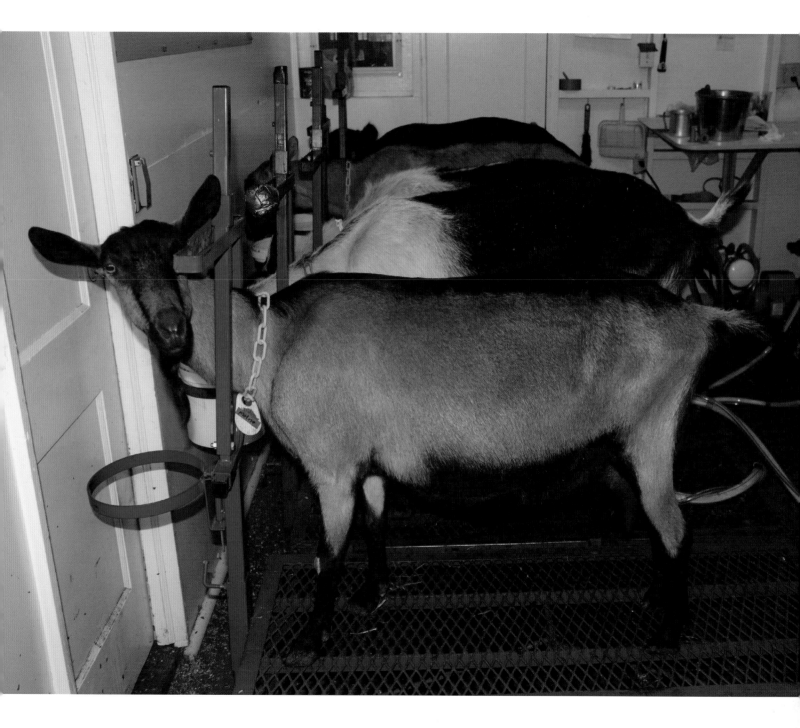

BIRTHING

When the birthing season comes around in March, I feel the excitement and the worry of an expectant mother again myself. I chuckle when people ask about the does' due dates; don't they remember their own deliveries? I'm too focused on the hope and anxiety I feel to be very concerned about the calendar. We can estimate but nature, flowing through the does themselves, makes the ultimate decision. The does can even sense an approaching storm and hold off laboring until after bad weather.

On whichever day the first birth happens, it generates all the excitement you'd expect. We alert the GoatKeeper sponsor families to stay tuned to the BarnCam, I start a phone chain to alert people to the impending deliveries, and even chance visitors may end up in the barn as an audience or accidental assistants. We're all drawn to the sheer wonder of it. And, no matter how exhausted I am, I can't wait to get my hands on each new baby, like I would a newborn child.

To ease a doe's work throughout labor and after delivery, I wipe the steaming kid dry or even use a hairdryer. The exhausted mother may be too distracted by another kid emerging to do the clean-up herself and the weather is still bitter cold. I also clear the kid's nose to ease its first breaths. When I see that certain arch of its back, I feel a jolt of joy because next, the kid will shakily stand and, within fifteen minutes of birth or so, take its first step towards its mother's milk. Those wobbly, instinctual steps are incredible, so tentative and determined. It's hard to resist the urge to press my nose against their irresistible pink one and feel the swirled markings of their silky hair. Soon after their first nursing, the babies contentedly close their big eyes and bed down, intertwined with their mother and each other for warmth. Their bunny-like ears peek over a nest of straw.

This spring brought forty kids in the first month of birthing —three sets of quadruplets were born on one day alone. Still, the swelling bellies of the rest of the herd made me tingle with nervousness and anticipation as I geared up for more. After nearly one hundred deliveries, I knew more deeply how many things can go wrong but also

the extraordinary marvel of how it turns out so often. The unknowns of each spring heighten my apprehension about each individual birth. Will my girls endure the pains well? Will the kids be strong?

Early in my farm career, I couldn't figure out why Faith was so weak in only her second breeding season. She had stopped eating for a couple of weeks and was not getting up. After consulting vets and other herders and trying many of their remedies, I couldn't reverse her deteriorating condition so I made the wrenching decision to put her down. That evening, Mark could see the tears in my eyes and held my shaky hands as we said goodbye to her. We waited together with the vet for Faith's peaceful, but not-so-quick death and prepared to dispose of her body. Before leaving the barn though, something inside told me to set the expecting Carly apart in a pen, even though she was a week away from delivering. Later that night, I just had an instinct to check on her again and there were her twins, resting together in the straw. They were born

a week early, on the night Faith died, as if to honor her. We named one doeling Tina and the other (You Gotta Have) Faith. Even now, these inseparable twin sisters, Tina and Faith, seek each other out and bed down together at night, uncannily kidding within days of each other each year.

Ten days into birthing this year, we hit a peak period for scheduled births. Four to six does were expected to drop their kids and the atmosphere at the farm was electric. Who would go first, would all go well? With the limited tools available to us, we cannot know in advance how many kids each doe will have and so we were just taking bets. Odds were on Macy birthing first with three kids, as she'd done in the past. We told Faith's GoatKeeper sponsor family to be ready but couldn't guarantee that anything would actually happen for them to see. Meanwhile, Melissa was lounging in an open paddock and due as well. Of course, it was a weekend, with Ron and Kevin off, but Kelly was on hand and we had lots of visitors. My daughter Bari was up from the city and our friend Cara, Mark and his assistant Michelle were all on the farm. This was also the Saturday Karen had decided to finally get

some video of the births so she trained her camera on Macy. By chance, vet Dan Hochman stopped by too with his two-year old. No action, no nothing all morning. Finally, Kelly called me; Faith was showing sure signs. Then she started, so quickly that her GoatKeepers had to watch the first birth on the BarnCam before they rushed over. When two more kids arrived, we were all delighted and laughing. I always watch carefully to be sure the placenta has been passed but Faith's behavior just didn't seem to reflect that. "If I didn't know better, I'd say there was another coming," I announced. As if on cue, there came her fourth, completing the farm's first ever set of quadruplets.

I blinked for one second and all hell seemed to be breaking loose! As usual, Tina was laboring in synch with Faith. I heard Cara wondering out loud, "Will she have four too?" But before I could reply, I realized we had babies all over the place! Four more and fireworks! Melissa started to labor then, distracting us from Tina. We were barely able to squeeze out the door of the barn to rush outside and check on her as well. Before long, her three kids were born smoothly too. Meanwhile, Karen left Macy, our watched pot, and tried her best to capture on

video all the births at once, maneuvering around us as we threw the clean towels to any hands willing to begin drying off the explosion of babies. We laughed, scrambled, wiped, congratulated ourselves and soothed the does. After all that, I lost my bet on Macy, who labored slowly all day and was the last to drop her four kids late that evening.

When I witness normal, multiple births like those or even miss a birth that a doe has accomplished without me, I'm humbled and reminded that the does often take care of this all by themselves. Sometimes, just patience and restraint are what's required while nature works with minimal assistance. When I'm watching the doe's body do what it needs to do and I see that little snout emerge, it's more than a miracle, cliché though that is. I'm so moved that I often can't help participating. With time and experience, I've learned small ways to help even when a birth is going well, like gently tugging on the does' teats to help to expel the placenta, moving the kids to nurse or tickling the kid's nose with a piece of hay to stimulate its breathing as the doe licks off its birth sac. I might feed the mother warm soy milk as an energy booster or clean up the doe's back end after birthing. I might help the babies to get up, walk to their mother and find her udder, murmuring encouragement all the while.

When a birth is difficult, nature doesn't care if I'm tired or sad. There's still work to be done and it must be done the right way. There's nothing I wouldn't do to try to save every member of my small herd. At least by now and by necessity, I've learned ways to help and to differentiate moments where I must intervene. More and more, I can rely on my own skills and instincts about what my animals need, which kid is not thriving, which doe is in pain, when they will go into labor and what might be going wrong.

This year, we tried many strategies to get Jewel to term when she faltered at the end of her pregnancy. One of my original girls, she was battling hard to stay alive. Like an ideal mother, Jewel gave everything of herself to her kids. She held on but continued to go downhill as her pregnancy progressed. We propped up her calcium and glucose levels but Jewel still went from a weakened condition, to going off feed, to needing fluids and then some. Eventually, even though we rushed her to the vet's for an emergency c-section, we lost not only her three kids, but Jewel as well.

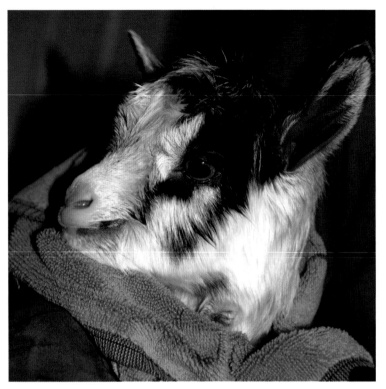

I had tried so hard to save her, my cornerstone doe whose life had taught me so much. Despite the long odds she had faced this season, this defeat hit me especially hard coming at the beginning of the kidding season, when I prepare myself to make many tough, right choices. I go to extraordinary lengths to save any animal, whether a key doe or a soon-to-be-sold buckling. Does this commitment disqualify me as a real farmer, who can dispassionately do what needs to be done?

Sometimes the does help me too by taking care of each other. More than once, I've seen one doe nudge a weakened sister to stand up. One sad morning I came into the barn to the heartbreaking scene of Shania's lifeless body and unexplained death, her four-week old kids curled up next to her. My heart soared though when I saw that Dione had stepped in to be Shania's surrogate, nannying and taking the orphans to nurse. Maybe in helping, she was comforting herself as well. Long after I'd separated them from her, Dione had cried mournfully for her own kids.

Birthing is also the time to begin the work of the new cheesemaking season. I have to start balancing the kids' needs with the milk I need for my cheese. They nurse for two weeks before I separate them from their moms in order to take a larger share of the milk. There's plenty to supply the kids with their mothers' milk by bottle-feeding for the next eight weeks. With regular milking, the does' udders and milk supply grow quickly. Still, sometimes the does' sad calls for their babies interrupt my thoughts as I walk up from the barn with cans of milk.

Holding the babies individually in our laps to bottle-feed them starts to socialize them in preparation for children, volunteers and other farm visitors. At first, I have to chase the kids around to get them to take a bottle from me. By day four though, they have figured out that

I'm the Alpha Doe with the food. Soon they are waiting at the gate and they swarm around me so that I must slowly push my legs in long strides through a tide of adorable, bleating babies as many as four times a day. Each time I hold and feed one, I fill up with new life. In the ocean of baby goats, we can already start to see their unique personalities and traits stand out. Sometimes the runts get the most attention. Kelly is a sucker for the weak ones like that and Karen plays favorites with the ones with white belted markings.

As anxious as I am to get started making cheese with their milk, separating the does and kids is also hard. At that point, I have to sell off certain doelings and nearly all the bucklings, probably to be eaten. I walk back and forth among them, judging the ones to keep or say goodbye to. I strike compromises as best I can by keeping more bucks than I probably should or by allowing each intern to adopt a kid to raise. These are the less-than-romantic but inevitable decisions we face each year.

MILK TO CHEESE

People often ask me how long it takes to make cheese. Actually, it takes five months to finally get enough milk to even start, from breeding to birthing to waiting for initial weaning. The less smart-aleck answer is at least three to four days for our simplest fresh cheese. Our bloomy

rind cheese needs around four to six days and at least another four days of ripening to get to our desired flavor profile. I may then make a judgment call of a day plus or minus to have the MontVivant either "chef ready" or prepared to sit in a retail store a little longer.

Truthfully, as a farmstead operation, the cheese starts with milking the does morning and evening, six at a time, in a routine they know well. After washing and hand-stripping their two teats, I gently attach the machine, which has replaced the hand milking, possible only when I had twelve goats. The machine may be less romantic but it has saved me from carpal tunnel damage. When the interns are trained, I get more relief but early in the season, I do this alone.

When the heavy cans of sloshing milk get to the cheese house, the ritual takes over with a welcome rhythm. Even on a hectic day, the smell of good cheese reminds me what the effort is all about and the day's tasks can bring me back to life. No matter how preoccupied or tired I feel, I have to watch the milk carefully. If all the other cheese house tasks distract me, I can easily lose the milk.

As I pick the cultures, I think about coaxing out a little more bloom, building more yeasty flavors or emphasizing mushroom-y ones. Stirring them in followed by the rennet is meditative and I count out loud to slow myself down as a sheen forms on the milk. Then, I decide which way to ladle the curd from the night before. Do we need to set MontVivant for Ken or Merdian for CAP today? I pour off the filmy excess whey and start to methodically ladle the curds into the round and pyramid-shaped molds. I position them to drain well and also top off the settled curd in other molds. I'm satisfied and pleased to see another batch of cheeses well on their way.

Meanwhile, Kelly and I attend to the business of flipping the finished cheeses, salting them, sprinkling the Meridian with ash, checking orders and wrapping cheese for customers. And there is always washing and more washing to do. The buckets, ladles and molds must be sanitized but I feel tremendous satisfaction when the fridge is finally stacked with dozens of chubby circles and pyramids.

The unending work of another spring has once again rewarded me with a new herd of spring kids, rows of hand-ladled cheeses, the green hope of the garden and the expanding community of the farm. The first taste of my pure, delicious and unique cheese reminds me why I do it all. ✐

The spring recipes and accompaniments in this chapter celebrate the season of birth and my return to that sweet smell of the cheese house. The season's flavors are delicate, fresh and renewing: new peas, asparagus, baby greens and lettuces. We sweep out heavier winter meals like we sweep the winter dust out of the barn to let in the new air and tender light.

SMOKED SALMON ROLLUPS

Fresh and clean, this preparation atop fresh cucumbers works as a carb-free alternative.

INGREDIENTS

16 ounces thinly sliced smoked salmon

8 ounces fresh goat cheese, softened

$1/2$ tsp lemon juice

small bunch of dill, chopped (reserve some sprigs for garnish)

pepper

small bunch of alfalfa sprouts or watercress or claytonia or baby mache

pumpernickel bread thinly sliced (optional)

lemon twists

DIRECTIONS

Whisk cheese to lighten and add dill and lemon juice. Pepper to taste.

Cut a piece of plastic wrap and place on work surface.

Line up salmon slices next to one another, overlapping slightly to form a rectangle.

Spread cheese mixture evenly over the salmon surface.

Working from the long side, tightly roll up salmon using the plastic wrap to help but be sure not to wrap it into the roll.

Secure ends and refrigerate roll for at least a couple of hours or overnight.

Slice the log into $1/2$" thick pieces.

Place rollups on their side—either on their own or on top of thin piece of pumpernickel bread (square or triangle).

If using bread, place small amount of desired green before placing rollup and garnish.

Garnish with dill sprig and lemon twist.

Yields 36 pieces

Note: It isn't necessary to make the salmon rectangle. Alternatively, you can spread cheese onto individual slices of salmon and roll them. Refrigerate until ready to serve.

HERBED ROLLUPS

This gives 'fast food' a new meaning—delicious and healthy too!

INGREDIENTS

$^1/_2$ bunch chives

1 bunch lovage

1 bunch parcel

8 ounces fresh goat cheese, softened

$^1/_2$ pound baby spinach washed & dried

4 soft whole wheat tortillas

DIRECTIONS

Wash and thoroughly dry herbs and mince.

Combine herb mixture with softened goat cheese.

Spread cheese evenly over tortilla.

Place one layer of spinach leaves over the cheese layer.

Roll up tortilla tightly.

Trim ends and slice remaining tortilla into $^1/_2$" pieces.

Place on tray with cut side facing up to show off pinwheel.

Yields 48 pieces

Note: Can substitute arugula for spinach.

CHICKEN & AVOCADO QUESADILLA

This South of the Border favorite is even better with goat cheese!

INGREDIENTS

8 ounces mushrooms, thinly sliced

3 Tbsp butter

8 large whole wheat tortillas

8 ounces fresh goat cheese

1 cup cooked chicken, shredded

1 ripe avocado, peeled, seeded and diced

fresh cilantro, minced

butter or oil for grilling quesadilla

salsa, your choice

DIRECTIONS

In a skillet, melt butter over medium heat.

Add mushrooms and sauté about 6 minutes until softened.

Place tortillas on work surface and spread evenly with goat cheese.

Layer half the tortillas with chicken, avocado, mushrooms.

Sprinkle with cilantro.

Place second tortilla on each and press gently.

Place small amount of butter in large non-stick skillet.

Cook one quesadilla until golden (about 2 minutes) and then flip.

Repeat for all tortillas.

Quarter and plate.

Serve with salsa.

Yields 4 servings as a main course but cut into eighths, serves at least 8 for hors d'oeuvres

Note: Roasted peppers and grilled onions make great additions to this dish.

49

HERBED SOUFFLETTES

Why not turn a lovely spring walk into a hunt for the central ingredient of your dinner? Forage in the woods near a wetland area and you'll be sure to find ramps or wild leeks. This evanescent onion is a real treat! But don't despair if you're not inclined to pick your own.

INGREDIENTS

6 eggs, separated

8 ounces fresh goat cheese

8 ounces milk (goat, whole or half & half)

$1/2$ cup all purpose flour

$3/4$ tsp salt

$1/2$ tsp pepper

4 Tbsp minced ramps (can substitute leeks or green onions)

2 Tbsp minced lovage (or parcel or thyme)

DIRECTIONS

Preheat oven to 350 degrees.

Lightly oil a 12 cup muffin pan.

In large bowl, whisk yolks and cheese until blended thoroughly.

Whisk in milk.

Add flour, seasoning and herbs.

In another bowl, beat egg whites until stiff.

Fold whites into cheese gradually in three additions.

Pour mixture into prepared tin and bake about 30 minutes until tops are golden.

Yields 12 full size (muffin) soufflettes

LEMON CHIVE DRESSING

Some call this 'Goat Goddess Dressing'—whatever you call it, it's a great harbinger of spring.

INGREDIENTS

8 ounces fresh goat cheese

$1/2$ cup goat milk (can substitute any milk)

2 Tbsp freshly squeezed lemon juice

1 tsp fine sea salt

$1/3$ cup chives, finely chopped

DIRECTIONS

Blend cheese and milk in food processor or blender until smooth and creamy.

In separate bowl, mix lemon juice and salt until salt is dissolved.

Combine 'cream' and lemon juice.

Add chives.

Refrigerate. (Will store 3-5 days.)

Yields 1 $1/2$ cups

Note: Pair with baby spinach, early radishes and mint from your garden!

Drizzle over the season's first asparagus, roasted or steamed.

MACHE SALAD WITH
HONEY LEMON DRESSING

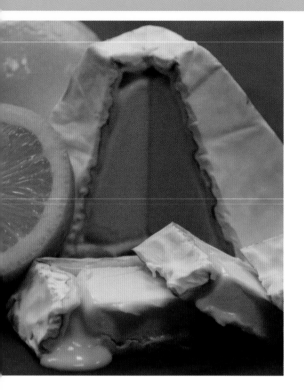

This delicate green, planted in the fall, loves the cool weather so it's ready for harvesting along with early spring cheese.

INGREDIENTS

1 Tbsp honey

Juice of half of lemon

$1/2$ cup balsamic vinegar

$1/4$ cup olive oil

salt & pepper to taste

6 ounces mache

4 wedges of MontVivant

DIRECTIONS

Combine the honey and lemon juice until emulsified.

Add vinegar and shake well.

Finally add the oil.

For a composed salad, toss the mache with desired amount of dressing and arrange the mache on the plate.

Salt & pepper to taste.

Place wedges of the cheese decoratively.

Yields 4 servings

Note: This dressing holds up well and doesn't break down before or after dressing your salad. This salad is perfect paired with a nice crusty baguette.

CRUSTLESS SORREL QUICHE

What's more spring than sorrel? And no crust, no calories. How can you beat this?

INGREDIENTS

2-3 cups sorrel leaves, chopped

$\frac{1}{2}$ bunch chives, minced

4 whole eggs

3 egg whites

2 cups 2% milk

3 Tbsp flour

6 ounces grated Fontina cheese

6 ounces ChevreLog, grated*

1 tsp nutmeg

salt & pepper to taste

DIRECTIONS

Butter the bottoms and sides of an 8" or 9" square baking dish.

In bowl, whisk whole eggs and egg whites together.

In second bowl, mix milk and flour together.

Combine both mixtures well.

Add nutmeg, salt & pepper.

Spread sorrel and cheeses evenly across baking dish.

Pour in egg/milk mixture.

Bake 25-30 minutes or until top is lightly browned and puffed.

Let cool for 10 minutes and serve.

*Try goat Gouda.

Yields 9 servings

Note: Baking in a square dish makes cutting into lite bites, sides or main course portions easier.

SPINACH GNOCCHI

As a first course or side, these gnocchi are fabulous with melted sage butter, tomato sauce or extra parmesan cheese.

INGREDIENTS

24 ounces baby spinach

16 ounces fresh goat cheese

1 cup parmesan cheese, grated

1 egg

$\frac{1}{2}$ cup (plus) all purpose flour

$\frac{1}{4}$ tsp nutmeg

salt & pepper to taste

DIRECTIONS

Blanch spinach, squeeze out excess water and chop.

Mix next three ingredients to form gnocchi base.

To make dough add only enough flour so dough is still sticky.

Divide dough into quarters and roll each into a 1" diameter rope.

Cut each rope into 1" pieces and roll off fork to form gnocchi.

Place gnocchi on flour dusted board until all are formed.

Bring pot of water to boil.

Cook gnocchi (without overcrowding) until gnocchi rise to top.

Cook another 3-5 minutes.

Remove gnocchi from water and drain.

Serve warm with your preferred topping.

Yields 4-6 main course servings

RAINBEAU CHARD GRATIN

Magnificent color and amazing nutrition are both packed into this all-season beauty!

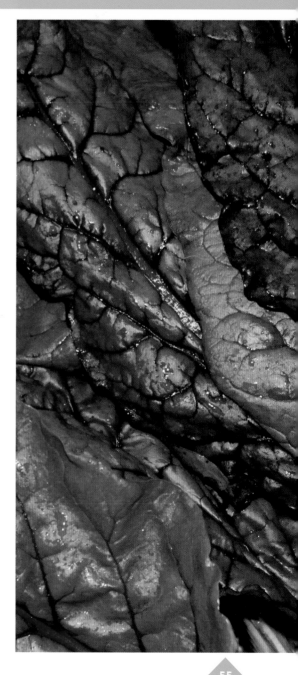

INGREDIENTS

4 Tbsp butter

$^3/_4$ cup fresh breadcrumbs

1 lb rainbow swiss chard, washed thoroughly

2 Tbsp olive oil

1 medium shallot finely chopped

2 -3 garlic cloves finely chopped

$^1/_4$ tsp nutmeg

salt & pepper to taste

4 ounces firm ChevreLog or MontVivant, grated

4 ounces Fontina, grated

DIRECTIONS

Preheat oven to 400 degrees and coat the interior of a 1 $^1/_2$-quart gratin or baking dish with 2 tablespoons of melted butter.

Spoon $^1/_2$ cup bread crumbs to coat the dish.

Slice chard stems into 1/2-inch pieces; chop the leaves separately.

Heat olive oil in a pot over medium heat, then add the shallot and garlic.

Cook, stirring constantly, until softened but not browned, about 1 minute.

Add the chard stems, sprinkle with salt and cook until just softened.

Add leaves and cook until the chard has wilted to half its original volume, about 2-3 minutes. Stir continuously.

Add nutmeg, salt and pepper, then toss with grated cheese.

Transfer to baking dish, spreading evenly.

Melt remaining 2 tablespoons butter and toss with $^1/_4$ cup bread crumbs.

Top vegetables with bread crumb/butter mixture and bake in oven until bubbling and topping is golden, about 20 minutes.

Yields 4-6 servings

SPRING PIZZA WITH FRESH ARUGULA

Made with a homemade crust as we do, or even an easy cheat from the dairy case, you can't resist these as snacks or a main meal.

INGREDIENTS

Pizza Dough* (recipe follows)

$1/4$ pound arugula, washed and dried with stems removed

2 Tbsp olive oil

$1/4$ cup pine nuts

6-8 ounces fresh goat cheese

DIRECTIONS

Preheat oven to 450 degrees.

Prepare dough according to recipe below.

Roll out dough as two 12" pizzas or 4 personal size pizzas on pizza stone or baking sheet.

Spread thin layer of arugula.

Drizzle with olive oil.

Break small amounts of goat cheese and place on top of pizza.

Spread pine nuts over surface of the pizza.

Bake 10-20 minutes.

Cool slightly.

Cut in wedges and serve hot.

Yields 4-6 servings

*PIZZA DOUGH

INGREDIENTS

1 cup water

1 package yeast

3 cups of flour

2 Tbsp olive oil

DIRECTIONS

In a small bowl, dissolve the yeast in warm water.

Combine mixture with half the flour.

Mix well.

Add the oil and the remaining flour and combine with your hands until thoroughly mixed.

On a lightly floured surface, knead the dough about 5 minutes until smooth, adding a little flour to make dough less sticky.

Place dough in lightly oiled bowl and cover with clean towel. Place in warm spot and let rise about 1 hour or until doubled in bulk.

Working on a floured surface, take risen dough, punch down slightly and divide into portions—two 12 inch pizzas or 4 personal size pizzas (fun for family pizza night or a buffet/make your own).

Roll each into a ball and let rest another 10 minutes.

Roll out dough into circle.

Continue with topping above.

Note: Can substitute tortillas or ready-made pizza crust.

STUFFED FILET OF SOLE WITH LEMON POTATOES & LEEKS

Michael Williams, Chef/Co-owner, The Perennial Chef, Bedford Hills, NY

INGREDIENTS

8 filets of sole skinned and deboned (approximately 2 1/2 pounds)

2/3 cup extra light olive oil

1 medium Vidalia onion, 1/4 inch dice (2 cups diced)

4 medium red potatoes, peeled & diced 1/4 inch (3 cups diced)

1 leek, white part only, 1/4 inch dice (1 1/2 cup diced)

1 lemon, juiced

salt & pepper

1 1/2 cups "dry" Italian white wine (Trebbiano, if possible)

2 cups Rainbeau Ridge fresh goat cheese

1/2 Tbsp minced fresh thyme

DIRECTIONS

Heat oil in a heavy bottom sauté pan over medium heat.

At the first hint of smoke, add the onions and stir.

Add 1 tsp salt and a pinch of pepper and reduce heat to low.

Sauté 5 minutes until the onions are translucent. (Do not caramelize onions; they should be without color.)

Add the diced potatoes and the juice of 2/3 lemon.

Stir and cover, continuing to cook at low temperature for 10 minutes.

This mixture should be stirred every few minutes to prevent the potatoes from sticking and also for even cooking.

Add diced leeks, stir and cover again for approximately 10 more minutes until the potatoes are fully cooked but not mushy.

Place mixture on a sheet pan and allow to cool to room temperature.

The potato mixture should be removed with a slotted spoon so as to leave the excess oil behind. Reserve the oil in the pan for the sauce and add the white wine.

Bring to a simmer and remove from heat, setting aside for now.

Preheat oven to 350 degrees and prepare a casserole dish with cooking spray.

To stuff the sole:

Place filets of sole on a sheet pan, presentation side down, with the thinner tail pointing away from you.

Place $1^{1}/_{2}$ to 2 Tbsp potato mixture near the thicker end of the filet

Place 2 Tbsp of goat cheese atop the potatoes.

Roll the filet with mixture inside, starting with the thicker end until the mixture is encapsulated.

Push in mixture from both sides to compact it and place in a casserole dish, seam side down (tail side down).

Repeat until all the filets are in the casserole.

Spoon the olive oil and wine mixture reserved in the pan over each fish.

Spritz the stuffed sole with remaining $1/_{3}$ lemon and sprinkle with a "light" touch of salt and the minced fresh thyme.

Cover tightly with foil and place in a 350 degree oven for approximately 25 minutes, uncover and bake another 5-10 minutes until done.

The sole will have decreased in size approximately 25% and will be firm to the touch.

Remove casserole dish and tilt to pool the sauce at one end and spoon sauce over hot fish repeatedly for about 2 minutes and serve with leftover potato mixture spooned atop fish.

Yields 8 servings

TORTELLINI WITH ASPARAGUS & BROWN BUTTER

THE GRAND TIER RESTAURANT

Jeff Raider, Executive Chef, The Grand Tier at Lincoln Center, New York, NY

CHEESE FILLING

INGREDIENTS

$1/2$ cup Rainbeau Ridge fresh goat cheese

$1/4$ cup sheep's milk ricotta cheese, strained

$1/4$ cup Parmesan cheese, grated

4 egg yolks, beaten until pale

1 cup fresh Italian parsley, chopped

1 small pinch chili pepper flakes

Kosher salt & fresh ground black pepper to taste

DIRECTIONS:

Mix together the cheeses.

Fold in the egg yolks and the parsley.

Season the mix with the chili pepper flakes, salt and pepper.

PASTA DOUGH

INGREDIENTS

4 cups semolina flour

6 whole eggs

1 tsp extra virgin olive oil

1 pinch kosher salt

DIRECTIONS

Mound 3 $1/2$ cups of the flour in the center of a large wooden cutting board.

In small bowl, mix together 4 of the eggs, olive oil and salt.

Make a well in the middle of the flour and pour egg mixture in the well.

Mix in the flour until the dough forms.

Knead the dough for five minutes.

Wrap the dough with plastic wrap and allow to rest for 30 minutes at room temperature.

Roll the pasta into thin sheets using a pasta machine.

Cut into squares.

Mix the remaining 2 eggs to create an egg wash.

Brush egg wash on the pasta squares.

Spoon the Cheese Filling in the center and fold into desired shape.

Cover with a damp towel and refrigerate for 30 minutes.

TORTELLINI

INGREDIENTS

20 tortellini

1 cup butter

4 fresh sage leaves

1 cup asparagus tips, blanched

$1/4$ cup Parmesan cheese, grated

Kosher salt & fresh ground black pepper to taste

DIRECTIONS

Melt the buter in a sauté pan with the sage until the butte is golden brown.

Drop the tortellini in a pot of boiling salted water.

When the tortellini floats to the top of the water remoe and strain dry.

Add the cooked tortellini and the blanched asparagus tips to the sauté pan with the brown butter and toss.

Season with the parmesean cheese, salt and pepper.

Serve warm.

Yields 4 servings

ARUGULA, PICKLED BEETS & WARM ALMOND COATED GOAT CHEESE SALAD

Theodore Roe, Chef, American Bounty Restaurant at the Culinary Institute of America, Hyde Park, NY

SALAD COMPONENTS

4 cups arugula, washed and dried

8 almond coated Rainbeau Ridge goat cheese discs (recipe below)

4 pickled red beets (recipe below)

4 pickled gold beets (recipe below)

Dijon vinaigrette (recipe below)

chopped fresh chives

salt & freshly ground black pepper to taste

DIJON VINAIGRETTE

INGREDIENTS

2 shallots, minced

1 Tbsp Dijon mustard

$2/3$ cups extra virgin olive oil

$1/3$ cup walnut oil

$1/2$ cups champagne vinegar

salt & pepper to taste

DIRECTIONS

In a blender or food processor, combine the shallots, mustard and vinegar.

While the machine is running, slowly add the walnut oil and olive oil to emulsify.

Season to taste.

PICKLED BEETS

INGREDIENTS

4 cups apple cider vinegar

3 cups sugar

1 Tbsp minced garlic

1 Tbsp minced ginger

1 tsp crushed red pepper

4 red beets, trimmed of greens and washed

4 gold beets, trimmed of greens and washed

DIRECTIONS

To make brine for the beets, in a stainless steel pot, boil the sugar and vinegar together, until the sugar is completely melted.

Remove from the heat, add the remaining ingredients, and steep for one hour.

Strain through a fine strainer and reserve for beets (or cool and refrigerate for later use).

Place the red and gold beets in separate pots and cover each with cold water, seasoning with kosher salt.

Bring to a boil, then turn the heat down to a lazy simmer.

Cook beets until you can pierce the beets with a fork with no resistance.

Strain the beets and run under cold water until the beets have cooled down.

Peel the skin, and cut into wedges.

Reheat brine if necessary and pour hot brine over each set of beets and allow to cool at room temperature.

(May be wrapped and stored in the refrigerator up to 10 days.)

It is best to cook the red and gold beets separately so the colors do not bleed together.

ARUGULA, PICKLED BEETS & WARM ALMOND COATED GOAT CHEESE SALAD (CONTINUED)

ALMOND COATED GOAT CHEESE

INGREDIENTS

8 ounces Rainbeau Ridge fresh goat cheese

$1/2$ cup roasted almonds, finely ground

$1/2$ cup finely ground unseasoned bread crumbs

2 egg whites

DIRECTIONS

Roll goat cheese into log, place in refrigerator for 30 minutes and then cut into 8 slices.

Mix ground almonds and bread crumbs in small bowl.

In separate bowl, whisk egg whites until slightly frothy.

Lightly coat each goat cheese patty in the egg whites, wiping off any excess, then place in the almond-bread crumb mixture and coat evenly.

Reserve the breaded goat cheese in the refrigerator until needed (they can be made 1 day in advance).

TO ASSEMBLE SALAD

Preheat oven to 350 degrees.

Place the breaded goat cheese onto a small baking pan and place into the oven for about 4 minutes.

Remove the red and gold beets from their brine and toss gently with some vinaigrette.

Arrange beets on plate.

Dress the arugula with the vinaigrette and arrange over the beets.

Place breaded goat cheese over the top of the salad.

Garnish with fresh cut chives and finish with fresh ground black pepper.

Add salt and pepper to taste.

Yields 8 servings

TANGY LEMON CHEESECAKE

The juice and zest of lemon highlight the tanginess of the freshest goat cheese.

INGREDIENTS

12 ounces fresh goat cheese

$3/4$ cup sugar

juice of $1/2$ lemon

zest of 1 lemon

1 tsp vanilla

6 eggs separated

4 Tbsp flour

   Optional: Fruit, including strawberries, peaches and blueberries,
      along with whipped cream and powdered sugar

DIRECTIONS

Preheat oven to 350 degrees.

Prepare 9" spring form pan with butter and dust with sugar.

Combine cheese, sugar, lemon juice, lemon zest and vanilla.

Beat until smooth.

Incorporate the yolks, one at a time.

Add flour until just combined on low speed.

In a clean bowl, beat egg whites until firm.

Add 1/3 of whites into the cheese mixture to lighten and then fold in
   remaining whites.

Pour batter into the prepared pan and bake until golden brown (about 45
   minutes).

Cool completely before serving.

Top with optional fruits and whipped cream.

Dust with powdered sugar.

Yields 8-10 servings

RHUBARB & STRAWBERRY COMPOTE IN A SHORTBREAD CRUST

The combination of the rhubarb and strawberries make this a delicious and beautiful dessert.

CRUST

INGREDIENTS

1 cup flour

2 Tbsp confectioners sugar

$^1/_2$ cup butter

DIRECTIONS

Preheat oven to 425 degrees.

Sift flour and sugar together into mixing bowl.

With pastry blender, cut in butter until mixture resembles cornmeal.

Chill for 30 minutes.

Remove from refrigerator and then press firmly into 9 inch pie pan.

Bake for 10-12 minutes and then cool to room temperature.

COMPOTE

INGREDIENTS

1 1/2 pounds rhubarb, washed, trimmed, and cut into 1/2 inch pieces

1/2 cup sugar

1/2 cup water

1/8 tsp ground cloves

1/2 pound strawberries, washed, hulled, and thinly sliced

DIRECTIONS

In a large saucepan, combine the rhubarb, sugar, water, and cloves.

Bring to a boil, cover, reduce the heat, and simmer 10 minutes, stirring occasionally.

Stir in strawberries.

Simmer for an additional 10 minutes.

Cool.

GOAT CHEESE CRÈME

INGREDIENTS

8 ounces fresh goat cheese

1/4 cup honey

zest half lemon

DIRECTIONS

Blend cheese, honey and lemon until creamy.

Set aside.

Yields 8 servings

Assembly:

Spread crème evenly on pastry shell.

Spoon compote over the top.

Slice and serve.

GOAT CHEESE ICE CREAM IN TUILES

Shhh! Don't tell anyone it's goat cheese. This is elegant when scooped into a homemade tuile and topped with fresh figs or your favorite fruit.

ICE CREAM

INGREDIENTS

- 2 cups whole milk or heavy cream
- 2-3 sprigs of rosemary
- $1/3$ cup honey
- 5 large egg yolks
- 4 ounces fresh goat cheese

DIRECTIONS

Warm milk in a saucepan over low heat.

Place rosemary sprigs in milk for about 10 minutes to infuse its flavor.

In a separate medium bowl, whisk together the egg yolks.

Remove the rosemary sprigs from the milk and then slowly pour the egg yolks into the milk, whisking constantly.

Stir the mixture constantly over medium heat with a heatproof spatula, scraping the bottom as you stir, until the mixture thickens.

Add the goat cheese and keep stirring until the cheese is melted and fully incorporated.

Chill the mixture thoroughly in the refrigerator, then freeze it in your ice cream maker according to the manufacturer's instructions.

TUILE

INGREDIENTS

- 2 egg whites
- $1/2$ cup powdered sugar
- $1/4$ cup melted unsalted butter
- $1/2$ capful almond extract
- $1/4$ cup flour

DIRECTIONS

Preheat oven to 325 degrees.

Line baking sheet with parchment paper and trace a series of 4" circles to guide your tuile.

Beat egg whites into soft peaks.

In separate bowl, cream butter and sugar.

Beat in almond extract.

Fold in egg whites.

Next, mix in flour until just combined.

Carefully spread mixture into 4" circles.

Bake 8–10 minutes or until edges are lightly browned.

Remove from oven and drape immediately over an inverted glass to form a cup.

Yields 6 servings

Assembly:

Let tuiles cool.

Fill each with small scoops of ice cream.

Top with freshly chopped figs or any other fruit.

STARTING WITH HERBS

EVEN IF YOU HAVE NEVER GARDENED BEFORE, even if you have only the smallest sunny windowsill, you can grow herbs. Herbs are a wonderful and ancient first step into pride of growership, the freshest flavors and culinary experimentation.

Many herbs such as cilantro (although mine always bolts fast to seed), dill and basil, can be started directly in the earth from seed. Popular woody herbs, such as rosemary, lavender or tarragon, are widely available in small pots to fill window boxes or integrate into flower borders. People have some success bringing them indoors in the cool weather too, depending on the interior microclimate of your house. Drying, freezing or putting herbs by in vinegars or jellies is easy in a home kitchen.

I never tire of classic combinations such as tomato with basil or sage in turkey dressing, but herbs also invite inventiveness. Try basil in an Asian cold noodle dish or that sage in an egg custard or pound cake instead. I have the learned the trick of adding herbs at the very end of cooking to maximize their aromatic contribution. I keep a good-sized herb patch just outside my kitchen door as was often done in English and French country homes, just to have the pleasure of stepping out to the kitchen garden to cut pungent, onion-y chives for a farm egg omelet, sprigs of spiky lemon verbena for our iced tea or a combination reminiscent of a favorite French salad. In the past, herbs were kept close also for home remedies; interest in this aspect of herbs as healers has returned. You can grow chamomile for tea to calm you or mint to wake you up.

At the farm, hearty perennial herbs are among the first hope-inspiring crops to show up after a long winter. Oregano mounds up and creeps everywhere; it can take a lot of moving and punishment and is essential to both the Greek and Italian palate. Thyme, and there are many types of thyme, also shows up early and likes to grow in rocky or root-bound pockets. It's terrific with poultry and in salad dressings. All the mints, so pretty and varied . . . apple, orange, peppermint, chocolate, spearmint, lemon . . . have to be beaten back with a stick too. Think juleps or mojitos, jelly to serve with lamb, and Reza Khorshidi's delicious cucumber salad recipe. Chives are also practically wild and will bloom into pretty purple, edible, clover-like flowers. Once you get these going, they'll take care of themselves and they'll tolerate some hours of shade too.

So let's say you get those four, oregano, thyme, mint and chives, established somewhere in your yard, here are three gotta have-'ems that don't reliably winter over in the Northeast:

Basil: Tender-leafed and ranging from the bushy three-foot Italian basil plants with broad, bright green leaves to compact Thai small-leaved purple plants, this staple needs plenty of sun. It's essential with tomatoes and available also bred to taste of lemon, anise, cinnamon or lemon.

Parsley: I prefer the flat-leafed Italian kind for its pronounced flavor but the curly style is also easy to grow and versatile. Either way, think beyond that curly sprig of garnish; whole salads just of parsley are a fixture of Middle Eastern cuisine.

Cilantro: This feathery herb can bolt to seed easily but reseeds itself. That seed in fact is coriander and it's that special flavor in Mexican and some Indian and Asian food. Chop a few tomatoes and peppers with it and add lime juice for almost-instant salsa. ❖

Four more to try . . .

Sage: Powerful, perennial and underused, the matte green or yellow or purple veined leaves can be fried quickly in olive oil for a stylish and delicious garnish to goat cheese.

Rosemary: It grows as sturdy hedges in warm climates and flowers prettily too. I mix it with our soft cheese and it's robustly paired with roasted meats.

Tarragon: I have a fond and unlikely memory of a French restaurateur in Tokyo who served a salad with tarragon, nuts and thin half-dollars of goat cheese that sang with freshness. The light licorice flavor of this herb is perfect with chicken.

Lemon balm: This easily-grown, ruffled-edged, light green herb goes everywhere lemon goes. It's probably best used fresh, rather than cooked.

BACKYARD CHICKENS

WHEN I MAKE A SOUFFLE or a sponge cake for Passover with my fresh farm eggs, the lightened batter almost spills over the edge of the pan because the egg whites whip higher and firmer. In the fry pan the deep yellow yolks sit high and round as teenager's perky breast and the whites even hold their form when you break the eggs into a hot pan. Freshness accounts for the aesthetic and taste difference; USDA-inspected eggs in the supermarket can be sold up to 30 days after their packing date. There's just no comparison between the farm-raised "Perfect Food" and store-bought, factory eggs.

It makes health as well as taste sense to choose local, free-range eggs. Research reports that free-range eggs (from hens that eat insects and plant materials outside) can contain about half as much cholesterol, up to twice as much vitamin E, and two to six times as much beta carotene (a form of vitamin A). For essential omega-3 fatty acids, free-range eggs can average four times more than factory eggs. Debate about eggs and dietary cholesterol goes on but it is now generally accepted that a normal diet can include a "common-sense" number of eggs as an excellent source of protein and other nutrients. An egg per day is healthy for people that aren't experiencing cholesterol or heart related health problems. And they are a relatively inexpensive source of protein.

We've kept chickens for additional reasons, years before I began farming seriously. I wanted to show my kids the sustainable system of garden scraps to chickens to eggs and chicken manure to garden. I wanted them to know that eggs weren't born in a styrofoam box.

In our case, the chicks came before the chickens and the eggs. Now I know more regional and local suppliers or sources for laying hens but then, I ordered our first brood from Murray McMurray Hatchery in Iowa, a well-known supplier. The chicks can be shipped from February to October with a minimum of 25 so that they keep each other warm. They can only be shipped on a Saturday and will have been enclosed with no food or water for as much as 48 hours on arrival. This meant that I had to romance our local post office to open on Sunday, to pay extra attention and to notify me when they arrived. Like the door of a speakeasy opening for the secret password, the back room was opened just for me. The postal worker gestured towards a peeping box. "I think those are yours," said the mailman.

Because it was easier to keep them warm, we kept them at home at first in an old playpen covered with chicken wire. After four or five days the fuzzy chicks sprouted pin feathers and they soon needed more space. Of course the powdery residue of their feathers was everywhere and their water and droppings had to be changed out regularly. At six to ten weeks they had become gawky adolescents. Not until four to five months did they take on the round feathered shape we associate with laying hens.

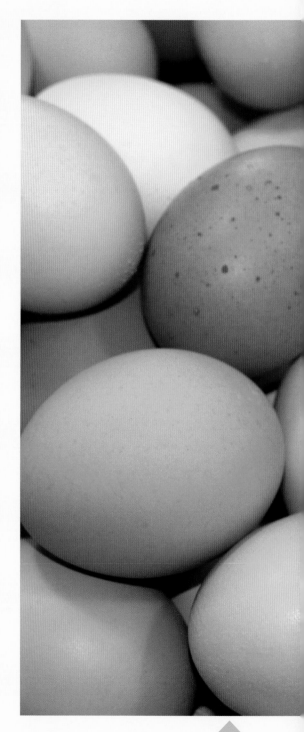

If cleaning and feeding chicks for four or five months seems too tricky for you, you can also begin with a new or used laying hen. The earliest hens will begin laying is at about four months and at their best, they will give about five to six eggs a week. However, even at 18 months, they will give an egg every other day, often enough for a family, and will live roughly three more years. Commercial egg farmers often sell their hens at 18 months because their production goes down but for backyard purposes, you'd still get plenty of eggs from the hens they rotate out.

You can also incubate fertilized eggs, as we did with our beautiful Bourbon red turkey, Fred, whose egg we bid for on ebay. Hatching eggs has become a popular project for elementary school classrooms in fact. It takes three weeks (twenty eight days for turkey and peafowl) of patient turning and maintaining heat and humidity at the right levels. The chicks won't all make it and up to 50% of them will be superflous roosters, who eat but don't lay. (A rooster is not necessary for hens to lay eggs.)

Now, I keep about four dozen Buff-Orpington, Barred Rocks, Rhode Island Reds and Araucana. In a dozen eggs, the colors range from cream to the deepest pinky-beige to aqua blue and almost olive green. The chickens support themselves not only by providing eggs to our farm's members and reducing garbage, but also by contributing fertilizer for the garden and by providing some pest control by eating ticks and other insects as they range free around the farm. The terms "cage-free" and "free range" mean little if the birds are not given enough room, clean, dry yards and the opportunity to eat what they need besides chicken feed.

We confine the hens to their roomy fenced yard and chicken house until midday so that every day isn't an Easter egg hunt; that is, so that they lay in their boxes. Still, we often discover one or two eggs elsewhere. In the afternoon every day, they are let out in complete freedom, heading for the compost pile, the hay bales and the lawn. Then, just like the cliché says, the chickens come home to roost as it darkens.

The children in our after-school farm programs (Sprouts) follow the hatching process as it happens and love reaching under the hens to gather the eggs. We also build curriculum around Things with Wings, which focuses on comparing the structure of our peacock, chicken and guinea hen feathers and on patterns in nature as a source for creative artwork for the children.

Interest in our backyard chicken workshops has grown. Of twelve participants who expressed serious intentions to keep chickens in our spring 2008 workshop, thirty percent were doing so within six months of the workshop. This year, many participants are coming back for more. We emphasize that it isn't hard, scary or burdensome and we prepare participants with information and resources.

To keep a few hens at home, you'll first need to check on local regulations. Between six to nine hens are enough to give five to six eggs daily, except in darkest January when egg production may stop as it's tied to available light. In addition to fresh water and food, the chickens need protection from swooping hawks, fox, skunks and raccoons as well. This may be the greatest challenge. Chicken house design can vary to fit a property but must be roomy enough to keep clean and not over-crowd the chickens.

You'll use your eggs as an integral ingredient in almost all desserts, from creme brulee to pound cakes, and in breakfast classics, such as omelets, French toast and eggs Benedict. Eggy main courses include quiche, cheese strata, fritatta and composed salads of poached egg, nestled in greens. Just don't try hard-boiled eggs. Because the fresh egg has not shrunk away from the shell inside, it's harder to peel. ❖

Farm Eggs . . .

- should be clean, unblemished and uncracked
- will have high, very orange yolks, especially if the hens eat garden scraps and insects
- will not spread out as much when cracked into a pan
- do not peel well for hard-boiled or deviled eggs
- are likely more nutritious
- are not the same product as "farm fresh eggs," as a supermarket box of eggs may be labeled
- taste fresher but subtly different from "factory' eggs

GARDENING WITH CHILDREN

GARDENING WITH CHILDREN IS PROBABLY the most obvious and effective way for them to understand sustainability and improve their eating as well. Watch a child pluck cherry tomatoes off the vine like candy, crunch happily on pea pods, string beans and refreshing baby cukes or carefully pick soft leaf lettuce that she has helped to plant, weed and grow. If your family is composting or adding waste from your own chickens to your garden, the cycle that feeds us becomes even clearer.

Of course, not all of us have the space or inclination for a full-bore vegetable garden at home; let's think small and accomplishable. In the spring, plan for a few cherry tomato plants, a bucket of herbs and another of leaf lettuce on a sunny deck. Even toddlers can help plant, water and harvest a homegrown salad.

Or, look for a community garden. The tried-and-true, wartime idea of an allotment garden, where gardeners each have a space and sometimes share resources, has been replicated in assisted living facilities, community centers, universities, churches and even business backyards. These gardens come with the bonus of expertise from fellow gardeners and can build a sense of intergenerational community around growing.

School gardens are an exciting newer phenomenon too that can improve school food and curriculum at the same time. When Alice Waters began her effort to improve school food in Berkeley, California, home of her legendary restaurant Chez Panisse, she began with a garden. Her Edible Schoolyard project grew into a foundation, which for twenty-five years now, has integrated curriculum, growing and eating in the Martin Luther King, Jr. Middle School, a Berkeley public school, and helps to set up school gardens all over the country.

Even without the four-season growing climate of Northern California, small-scale projects in a school's greenhouse, an interior courtyard or a cluster of wood tubs can grow enough for a celebration at least, if not for every lunch period. There are resources all over the internet now that will answer your questions about organizing to start a school garden, about creating garden-based lessons across the curriculum or about how gardens can be linked to improving school food.

The awareness grown in the garden is as important as the lettuce after all, as are the life-long habits of good health and environmental stewardship. Programs related to the garden might include a buddy program between older mentors and novice gardeners, an annual farmers market, a bird or insect count, garden art—such as designing row markers or scarecrows—experiments in plant propagation and cooking classes.

The success of our summer and after-school programs, Sprouts (Roots and Buds), which have become almost an institution in our area, speaks to the hunger young families have to put their children in touch with the land and seasonal cycles. Children collect maple sap and make maple syrup for their pancakes, touch the new goat kids, feel the lanolin under the sheep's wool, gather eggs, garden in their own plot and cook what they grow, beginning as young as two years old. Related hands-on projects foster creative and critical thinking. The message of sustainability to their enthusiastic families is vital and rewarding.

In your own area you might locate farm-based educational programs for children. Many farms offer summer programs, farm days or working farm vacations for the whole family. ❖

Several public schools and daycare centers in the towns around Rainbeau Ridge have created learning gardens, often maintained by volunteers over the summer months when the schools are closed. At the Mt. Kisco Daycare Center, for example, the elderly and the toddlers garden and eat together.

SUMMER

CADENCE AND
CONTENTMENT

Did I really hear my name called? When the judge announced Rainbeau Ridge a winner in a fresh goat cheese category, I had one of those dream-like moments. Did that really happen? In the first year I had entered, I had won a third place award for my lightly ash-coated Meridian at the American Cheese Society's annual judging. Early on it had been enough that my family recognized a good batch. Next, my customers' enthusiasm kept me going. I even told myself that I was satisfied with the approval of a professional independent evaluator before the ACS judging. His highly trained observations of the structure of the cheese gave me new insight for improvements. But at the moment I heard my name called, I suddenly found myself all smiles, elated, thrilled. Receiving the award did matter. With that gold sticker, the industry had recognized me as a successful cheesemaker and I had hit a personal prime. I was already determined to improve and resubmit my cheese another year.

IN THE SUMMER, 6 A.M. MIGHT be the only breezy, fresh moment of a day. On that kind of day, the sun can punish us with temperatures in the high 90s when anybody would rather be in a lake than in the goat barn. I run fans everywhere, I'm stripped down to a T-shirt and my hair is permanently clipped up off my neck. The animals lay low and look for shade and the garden wilts until evening watering. Even so, there's a comfortable momentum of harvesting, bed-tending, reseeding and new taste surprises arriving every week. The relentless piling on of springtime has eased and we've found a steady rhythm of work. We're up to speed and are hitting our stride.

As the pace stabilizes and I'm not up all night birthing or worrying, I might actually have a moment for a tall iced tea and a long look up at the brightest blue skies. I even start to miss the babies a little since they've all grown beyond bottle-feeding. When I first lift the window shade on the cheese season, I am coping, balancing and promising. By summer we have a predictable supply and demand of milk and cheese. All the girls are on the milk line at peak production and most post-kidding veterinary problems are resolved. Milk is coming in at over a gallon a day per doe and cheese is going out at roughly four hundred pieces per week. The cheese house is humming with the daily routine of pasteurization, culturing, molding, draining and so on.

Bedraggled from the heat of the milking room, I wave at a CAP customer on my trip to the cheese house to begin the morning's process. She beckons me over to tell me how beautiful the vegetables are that week and to rave about a new cheese I set out for sampling. I'm beaming and rejuvenated by her praise, the steady stream of visitors and the give and take in our farm community. That joy and pride is what makes the struggle for my own sustainability worthwhile and I might even have a spare moment to catch my breath and savor it.

In the summer, I'm also relishing my cheese every day. It makes every fresh, new product of the garden taste even better. In early summer, a fast-food lunch for me is ChevreLait and arugula, or my unmolded, soft cheese mixed with the bracing bite of chives, lovage and parcel, either slathered on good bread. As the summer goes on, I can substitute smoky grilled squash, sharp basil, (yippee!) sliced Cherokee and Zebra heirloom tomatoes and eventually roasted Golden Treasure and Rooster Spur peppers and Listada de Giandia eggplant. I play with mixing in lavender, coriander seed or rosemary to underline the tang of the soft cheese or coat a round with toasted pecans to emphasize the sweet notes.

The maple and hemlock trees in front of the farmhouse are shady gathering spots for the teachers and the Sprouts, Roots and Buds, who

don't seem to feel the heat the way adults do. The children arrive every morning, jabbering about the garden chores or the animals. Their parents tell me how even toddlers look for their rubber boots and ask hopefully, "Farm today, Mama?" Lettuce seeds that the children have planted yield countless mouthfuls as we've cut the leaves and let them come again. Carrots have developed "shoulders" that the children know to look for before pulling these gems from their underground home. Watching them pick and weed, it's easy to see what a gift it is to children to be free in the garden. Permission to garden without "no's" teaches them to enjoy the fruits of their labor literally, popping cherry tomatoes like candy. They walk boldly into the chicken yard and head to the feather-footed hen who they know will let them pick her up. The same children who said "No way!" at the beginning of a session have to be dragged out of the goat paddock when it's time to go. Now, the children seek out their special four-legged friends and embrace them both tenderly and playfully. For nicknames, I draw the line at teen divas like Brittany or Hannah Montana here, but the Sprouts usually prefer the predictable Oreo or Cookie anyway. I feel as proud as their parents of the assurance they've gained.

CAP is in full swing. Every week on shopping days, my chest swells with pride and satisfaction like one of the roosters'. Displayed in rustic buckets or baskets, our vegetables look like lush Flemish still lifes. Isaac and I listen to feedback carefully as our shoppers cluck happily over the beautiful produce, the cheese samples, our eggs, the recipe sheets and the bread, tarts and jams of

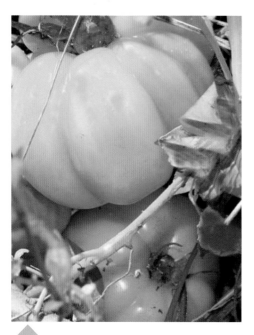

our carefully selected outside vendors. Members bring along out-of-town guests to show off the farm as if it were their own or, at least, their special secret.

In real ways, the farm is almost a substitute for what village life used to give us. It has become an access point, a place to trade information and news, recipes and gardening tips. Members' weekly visit is not just a transaction; it's a moment to be a part of something. I feel this when they delight in choosing their summer squash or Asian greens, when they notice or ask questions and when they pause together at the farmhouse windows to enjoy the view of the farm for a few more minutes. Member Whitney Brown is part of every program on the farm. "When my family moved here from my hometown of Chicago, the farm became my lifeline to settling into my new community. The farm is not trendy, clubby or judgmental because Lisa does such a good job of appealing to everyone. Really, Rainbeau Ridge benefits our whole family and embodies the best of living in this area. "

Our Open Farm Days, every Saturday from Memorial Day to Labor Day, bring even more people in touch with the farm. This broader community still marvels to discover our unexpected hidden treasure snuggled into the suburbs. Like the friends of the Little Red Hen, casual visitors can help me enjoy the farm, even if they didn't plant a seed.

Everyone celebrates the tomato plants that now cascade over the supporting cages and bear hundreds of flowers and fruits. Those first tomatoes usually ripen around here for a July 4th salad with Meridian or MontVivant. Customers can't get enough of our twenty-odd tomato varieties with quirky or old-fashioned names like Aunt Ruby's Green, Beams Yellow, Dr. Wyche's Yellow, Black from Tula, Black Sea Man, Black Krim and Nyagous. The bounty of shapes and sizes, from pale

rose to deep-red, from tiny jewels to bumpy full-pounders, is just the beginning. The indescribably alive taste of these tomatoes pierces through what we understand sadly that we have been accepting in the supermarket. For some of us, it revives the memory of long-ago summer tomatoes too. These timeless heirloom tomatoes cry out from the vine, "Eat me! Slice me! Dice me! Sauce me!" With the peak of the season at hand, we all happily oblige.

Farmers markets also get me closer to my cheese customers in the summer. While the markets involve a long day of packing, unpacking, setting up, standing, selling and repacking, they provide immediate feedback. The personal contact is worth the extra work. My customers identify me with my product, made so close by, and I can get to know them too while I hand out that cheesecake recipe or suggest pairing cheeses with the local cherries, smoked trout or salad greens from the stalls next to me. I start to recognize the regulars and these returning customers can discuss the fine points of the cheese nearly as passionately as I do.

Expanding further into retail and restaurant outlets means the challenge of new customers and critics and, of course, I've had disappointments. A chef orders once and never calls back. A respected Manhattan cheese shop says no thanks. It's hard work to deliver a farmstead cheese at its best each time and explain to a customer that the next batch may be ten days away. I never want to let them down. Nevertheless, the reaction of chefs and shop owners I do supply is so rewarding and demand for the cheese has steadily grown. Much like the circle of sustainable farming, I nurture the chefs and the stores I supply and they help us grow. I make sure they have what they need by keeping them in my production loop so they know how to plan and promote the cheeses.

Other signs too help me feel I've arrived. Cowgirl Creamery, a leading cheese shop in Washington, DC, is delighted to hear that that they'll be among my season's first deliveries. Michel Nischan's chef

de cuisine at The Dressing Room in Westport, Connecticut is calling me, rather than vice versa. After barely three years of being certified for retail sale, I'm now getting unsolicited calls from cheese shops on Long Island and restaurants in Virginia. But at first, it was a different story. Even though I'd passed inspection and was certified for retail sale, it took some guts to sell my cheeses.

MY FIRST CUSTOMERS

Phil McGrath, owner of the Iron Horse Grill in nearby Pleasantville, made it easy for me. An early supporter and a true believer, he continues to be a great customer, creating new ways to use the cheeses every year.

Hard-working and community-minded Joe Di Mauro was moving his Mt. Kisco Fish store and expanding to include local products. As an entrepreneur, he could relate to my business and had enough faith to take a flyer on me when

Since the start of my career in the city, I've looked for local products and used the cachet of local as a marketing tool. It's what I do. Lisa has always been so dedicated to the unbroken chain, the A to Z of the process. That guarantees quality; that's key. She even delivers the cheese in a straw basket. Lisa and I accommodate each other and we're loyal. I try to cultivate that relationship with all my purveyors over time. It's symbiotic. We make customers aware of Rainbeau Ridge's cheese, made just ten miles up the parkway in Bedford Hills, and Lisa promotes the restaurant. This year we're going to stuff agnolotti with ratatouille and "chevrecotta," using the Chef's Choice.

—Phil McGrath

When Lisa first came into the shop, I thought, "OK, here's another one." So much fresh American goat cheese has a cultured, ascorbic acid taste. But her cheese blew me away. I could taste the quality and integrity of the milk. She is doing it the right way: *moule a louche;* that is, hand-ladled curd, not extruded into logs, not a commodity. Great ingredients make great cheese. And Lisa listens. I told her straight out that our customers would want more salt in her cheese. We interact and tweak recipes; we talk about the conditions of the cheese at that moment. She delivers weekly and doesn't establish relationships she can't follow through on.

—Ken Skovron

I was ready to go public. Now Joe orders three or four dozen pieces twice a week in season. His Mt. Kisco restaurant, the Fish Cellar, also features our cheese.

Another key believer was Mona Spilo, proprietor of the nearby Bedford Gourmet Shop, whom I stalked in a local supermarket parking lot one day. I saw a silver 4x4 in the lot with the license plate "FROMAGE." I took a deep breath and looked for the car's owner. Whoever she was, her plate was a good sign and I needed to tell her about my cheese even before it was legal to sell. She said she would be very interested when I would become licensed and even drove back to the farm with me to see it.

Towards the end of my first full season, I summoned the courage to ask for some challenging feedback. I approached Ken Skovron, owner of the Darien Cheese Shop in Connecticut and tops in the business. Ken has been a bona fide, respected cheesemonger for over twenty years, a pioneer and believer well before the current and increasingly sophisticated local food revolution. He believes in American artisanal cheeses and really educates his customers about them. Would my cheeses meet his standard and would he carry them? In his well-stocked shop, I tried to calm my nerves and ready myself as I tentatively unfolded the imperfect packaging.

When Ken tasted the plain chevre and immediately described the cheese as crisp, clean, pure and "the full expression of the milk," I understood that he could tell how I value the farmstead process of my cheeses. He appreciated how I can respond to the needs of my herd and keep the smallest possible distance between the milk and the cheese it becomes.

VARIETY AND FINE TUNING

Paradoxically, every batch I make has to be consistent but not identical, meeting expectations but also reflecting the nuance of the time of year. In addition, over time the herd evolves so the milk is different; my techniques and the culture have matured. The *terroir* of Rainbeau Ridge is emerging, meaning that the particularity of the product relates directly to our microenvironment. Recently, I feel we have perfected our core product, the ChevreLait, a small, simple round, which "captures the essence of goat milk in cheese," much as Skovron described it.

I can only introduce a new cheese slowly to my customers because I want to be sure of continuity of supply and consistency of production and quality and that takes time. I might taste an exciting cheese with Ken and try to figure out how close I could come to its taste and texture, given my own milk, climate and cultures. Sometimes I get an accidental cheese, for example, a long-neglected, hard piece that could be grated. But could I replicate it? The romance of cheese also has a reality.

I've considered the long experiment of an aged raw milk cheese. First, I'd have to allocate milk for that and not sell it as our current cheese. Since demand is strong, an experiment would take money out of our till. In addition, the process of making hard cheese is not like testing a cake or a stew. I'd have to wait through three to six months of aging to discover the successes or failures. Then, with the season one-third over, I'd be waiting again for the result of each change I decided to make.

It took an electrical outage at the farm two years ago to create my current MontVivant pyramid. The power went out before the milk had cooled down, which meant I would not legally be able to use that batch of milk for fresh cheese. I seized the moment to try a bloomy rind mold, in the French tradition I had learned from, by adding an additional culture to the vat. The result was an exciting cheese with terrific potential. The mold blooms after four to five days and then we babysit these pyramids ten days before selling them to make sure the rind hasn't gone rubbery or separated from the inner cheese.

At two, four or six weeks of aging, or *affinage*, this pasteurized milk

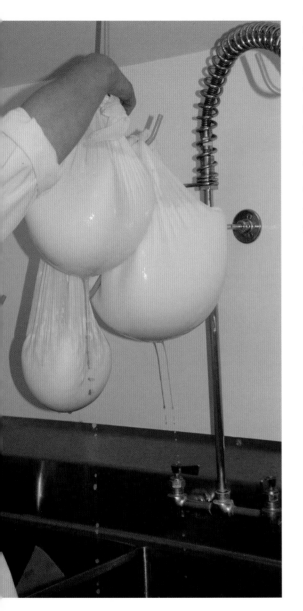

cheese takes on other properties, forming a cream just under the thickened rind and a *pâté* in the center. Unfortunately, I don't have several temperature and humidity-controlled rooms for consistent *affinage*. Because space is at a premium, I am constantly jockeying with the temperature inside and outside and with the draining and drying to create ideal conditions for the controlled spoilage I need. I can hardly keep the cheeses aging two weeks before customers are asking for them. They buy and age the MontVivant longer themselves. In recent years, demand for the MontVivant grew so I made the RondVivant, a nearly one-pound wheel, and the easy-to-slice ChevreLog shape of the same formula. (See the Cheese Primer for more details on our cheeses.)

What is Affinage?

Affinage is the art, not science, of aging cheese and encouraging the development of its more mature flavors. With the right facilities and manpower, affinage can happen on the farm. In addition, as is often the case in France, a committed cheesemonger or even chef will age a cheese himself after purchase from the farm. He must know the cheese well at its various stages and sell it or serve it too at that optimal moment. It's tricky to bring a cheese to its prime, by turning, watching and adjusting the temperature and humidity of an aging room or cave. In other countries, they use traditional straw or wood for aging racks, which are part of full flavor development.

With the establishment of the summer rhythms of regular harvest, weekly children's programs, ample milking and cheese production and sale, I'm able to focus on my greatest passions at Rainbeau Ridge, the goats and the cheese. With them, I become part of recovering the age-old art of saving precious milk by turning it into simple cheese and at the same time, I have created a unique and original product that expresses perfectly my goats' milk and my care for them.

The recipes in this section connect to the heat of summer and the unmistakable tastes of freshness in the garden. The incomparable tomato is queen but there's almost nothing in the garden that doesn't taste even better with goat cheese.

FAVA BEAN DIP

It may seem like a long way to go for your finished beans, but they are super healthy, delicious and gorgeously green.

INGREDIENTS

2-3 pounds fresh fava beans (shelled and skinned—net about 2 cups)

4 cloves fresh garlic, chopped

olive oil

1 tsp lemon zest

2 Tbsp lemon juice

$1/4$ cup water

5 ounces fresh goat cheese

salt & pepper to taste

DIRECTIONS

Prepare fava beans by removing from pods and blanching.

Rinse in cool water and drain.

Remove skins and set aside.

In sauté pan, heat olive oil over medium heat.

Add garlic and cook until just beginning to brown, then remove from heat.

In food processor, place peeled beans and process.

Add sautéed garlic, lemon zest, lemon juice and pulse until smooth.

Slowly pour about 1-2 tablespoons of olive oil.

Add goat cheese and quickly pulse until well combined.

Salt and pepper to taste.

Cool.

Serve with toasted bread, crackers, pita or pita chips.

Yields about $1^1/_2$ cups

PIQUILLO PEPPERS STUFFED WITH GOAT CHEESE

John Ash, Chef/Food & Wine Educator, Sonoma, CA

Use a good fresh goat cheese with herbs or mix in your own favorite fresh herbs to plain goat cheese. Piquillo peppers are available canned or jarred. See notes on why they are so special!

INGREDIENTS

10 ounces Rainbeau Ridge fresh herbed goat cheese

1 tablespoon lemon zest, finely grated

12 whole piquillo peppers

$1/2$ cup fragrant extra virgin olive oil

3 large garlic cloves, peeled and thinly sliced

Garnish: Basil oil and caper berries

DIRECTIONS

Preheat oven to 350 degrees.

Mash the goat cheese in a bowl with the lemon zest.

Stuff the whole piquillos three-quarters full with the mixture.

In a small saucepan, heat the olive oil over moderate heat and fry the garlic until lightly browned.

Remove the garlic, while reserving the oil.

Place the stuffed peppers in a pie plate in a single layer and spoon some of the reserved garlic oil over.

Bake peppers in oven until they are hot and the cheese is very soft, about 8 minutes.

If cheese oozes out just push it back in.

To serve, use a spatula to transfer peppers to a platter or individual plates.

Drizzle a bit of the oil over.

Spoon a little basil oil around and serve with a caper berry or two.

Yields 6 portions

Wonderfully versatile piquillo peppers come exclusively from the small northern Spanish region of Navarra. Nestled between the borders of southern France and Basque territory, the town of Lodosa thrives on a busy trade in piquillo peppers. The peppers take their name from their distinctive, narrow, triangular shape: Piquillo means "beak" in Spanish.

At first glance, piquillos look like a variant of sweet bell pepper, but just one bite will tell a different story, as the familiar sweetness gives way to a sneaky heat. Navarra's piquillo peppers are traditionally roasted over a beechwood fire, which adds a delectable smokiness to their bouquet. The final product is then packed whole in its delicious juices, ready to be sliced, stuffed and puréed into a variety of delicious dishes.

ROASTED TOMATO BRUSCHETTA

If you don't have the inclination or time to roast your own tomatoes, use fresh ones—but remember to roast some up for another time!

INGREDIENTS

1 small loaf of French bread sliced into ¹/₂ inch thick pieces

4 tsp olive oil

4-6 cloves of garlic

10 plum tomatoes

6 ounces fresh goat cheese

Optional: Fresh herbs—basil, oregano or thyme

DIRECTIONS

To prepare tomatoes:

Ahead of time, slice tomatoes in half the long way.

Toss in olive oil and salt liberally.

Place on a baking sheet lined with a silpat or sprayed with cooking oil

Roast at 250 degrees for 3 hours.

To prepare bread:

Preheat oven to 300 degrees.

Brush olive oil on both sides of slices.

Place bread slices on baking sheet.

Bake until golden (about 10 minutes), flipping over about halfway through cooking time. Remove toasts from oven.

Note: No tomatoes? Don't let that stop you! Keep a jar of roasted peppers on hand. Also, sauté up some rainbow colored swiss chard and use that instead—let your imagination go.

To prepare bruschetta:

Halve garlic cloves and rub top side of the toasts.

Raise oven temperature to 350 degrees.

Spread goat cheese over toasts.

Add a layer of roasted tomato.

Place on baking sheet and bake 10-15 minutes, until cheese is softened.

Can sprinkle with herbs—basil, thyme and or oregano.

Yields 24 pieces

ROASTED BEET SALAD

Roasting is the method of choice for so many vegetables as it brings out the sweetness and overall flavor. Beets are no exception, especially when paired with the cheese.

INGREDIENTS

6 beets—3 red and 3 golden make a wonderful visual combination

4-6 ounce piece of ChevreLait or Meridian goat cheese, cubed

$1/4$ cup pine nuts, almonds or walnuts, toasted

Dressing:

1 heaping tsp of Dijon mustard

2 Tbsp tarragon or white wine vinegar

$1/4$ tsp of dried tarragon

$1/2$ tsp salt

pepper to taste

DIRECTIONS

Wash beets and wrap tightly in tin foil.

Roast in 350 degree oven for $1 1/2$ hours.

Beets are done when they pierce easily with the tip of a knife.

Remove from oven and let cool slightly until you are able to handle them.

Unwrap foil and skin will slip off.

Cube to desired size. (Cut evenly for a more refined presentation.)

For dressing, combine ingredients and whisk until thoroughly combined.

Toss beets in a bowl with dressing and add cubed goat cheese and nuts.

Serve on a bed of greens as a side or starter.

Drizzle with olive oil or dressing.

Yields 4-6 servings

Alternative Presentation: Slice beets along the 'latitudinal' lines and layer goat cheese between beet layers.

FENNEL SALAD WITH
FRIED SAGE & ARUGULA

Every component of this salad is spectacular on its own, but together the harmony is really fantastic!

INGREDIENTS

4 ounces pine nuts

small bulb fennel

juice of half a lemon in one quart of water

small bunch fresh sage leaves

olive oil for frying

ChevreLog

5 ounces baby arugula

salt & pepper

DIRECTIONS

In a 350 degree oven or small skillet, toast the pine nuts until lightly brown, being careful not to let them burn.

Slice off the fennel stem tops and root, then halve lengthwise.

Using a peeler or sharp knife, slice as thinly as possible.

Soak in lemon water while you are preparing the rest of the salad.

Add olive oil in sauté pan (enough to generously coat the bottom) and heat to medium.

Spread sage leaves evenly in pan and fry gently until crisp but not brown; remove from pan and drain on paper towel.

Drain fennel and toss with the arugula in a large bowl with a little olive oil.

Salt & pepper to taste.

Top with slices of the ChevreLog, the pine nuts and some chopped fennel fronds.

An alternative presentation is to lightly dress the arugula in olive oil. Arrange on the plate. Place slices of cheese decoratively and mold drained fennel on top. Sprinkle with nuts.

Note: Raw fennel must be shaved thinly. For this salad, I prefer the lengthwise shave. Most recipes call for horizontal slices.

STUFFED SQUASH BLOSSOMS

These fragile golden blossoms are understated in flavor but are attention-grabbing on the plate.

INGREDIENTS

12 ounces fresh goat cheese

1 Tbsp basil, minced

1 tsp oregano, minced

1 tsp thyme, minced

2 eggs

water

flour for dredging

1 cup dry breadcrumbs

olive oil for frying

20 fresh squash flowers

DIRECTIONS

In medium bowl, thoroughly blend cheese, herbs and one egg.

Stuff each blossom with about 2 teaspoon of cheese batter, twist the end closed and set aside.

Mix remaining egg with water.

Pour enough olive oil in fry pan to about $1/4$" deep and heat over medium flame.

In the meantime, lightly dredge the stuffed blossoms in flour and then dip gently in egg wash before coating in breadcrumbs.

Lightly fry in olive oil until golden brown. Serve immediately.

Yields 20 pieces

Note: Blossoms are fragile and are best picked early in the morning. Rinse blossoms gently. Pat dry. Remove any external green leaves and internal pistil and stamen, using a sharp knife. Take care not to tear the blossoms.

TOMATO SALAD WITH CUCUMBER & MINT

Reza Khorshidi, Chef/Co-Owner, Rebeccas, Greenwich, CT

VINAIGRETTE

INGREDIENTS

2 Tbsp sherry vinegar

1 Tbsp wine vinegar

4 Tbsp grapeseed oil

4 Tbsp olive oil

$1\frac{1}{2}$ tsp Dijon mustard

$\frac{1}{2}$ cup chicken stock

salt & pepper

DIRECTIONS

Mix together the sherry and wine vinegars.

Add the grapeseed and olive oils.

Whisk in the Dijon mustard and chicken stock.

Add salt & pepper to taste.

SALAD

INGREDIENTS

4 tomatoes, peeled and sliced

2 hot house cucumbers, seeded and diced

$\frac{1}{2}$ cup mint leaves, minced

1 Vidalia onion, diced

4 ounces Rainbeau Ridge ChevreLait

DIRECTIONS

In a salad bowl, mix the cucumber, mint and Vidalia onion with 2 tablespoons of vinaigrette.

Yields 4 servings

Assembly:

Arrange tomato slice on each plate.

Layer $\frac{1}{2}$ of the cucumber salad on tomato and then top with another tomato slice.

Pour 2 tablespoons of vinaigrette.

Place slice of goat cheese on top of salad.

Add salt & pepper to taste.

TOMATO, WATERMELON & MERIDIAN TART

Dan Barber, Executive Chef/Co-Owner & Adam Kaye, VP Culinary Affairs, Blue Hill at Stone Barns, Pocantico Hills, NY

INGREDIENTS

4 rectangular slices of watermelon, 1" wide by 4" long by 1/4" thick

2 cups mixed heirloom cherry tomatoes, cut into quarters

1 wheel of Rainbeau Ridge Meridian, sliced very thinly, about 1/8" thick

About 8 leaves of basil, thin chiffonade*

1 Tbsp extra virgin olive oil

2 tsp red wine vinegar

salt & pepper to taste

DIRECTIONS

Heat a cast iron skillet or griddle over high heat for about 5 minutes.

Sear the watermelon slices for about 20 seconds on one side and remove from pan onto a small plate.

Place in the refrigerator to keep cold.

In a small bowl, season the tomatoes with the oil, vinegar, salt and pepper.

Trim the slices of Meridian to the width of the watermelon slices and arrange on top of each slice of watermelon in a single layer.

Place each slice of watermelon on four separate plates.

Carefully top each of the "tarts" with the marinated tomatoes.

Divide the basil chiffonade among the four tarts and serve.

*See Stuffed Chicken Breasts recipe for chiffonade instructions.

Yields 4 servings

BASIL CREPES

Make a double batch of these crepes while you're at it. Freeze them for when you're in a pinch but want to show off for those drop-in guests.

INGREDIENTS

1 cup water

1 cup milk

1$^{1}/_{2}$ cups flour

4 eggs

3 Tbsp olive oil, plus more for crepe pan

$^{1}/_{2}$ tsp salt

5 Tbsp minced fresh basil (or parcel, chives or lovage)

16 ounces fresh goat cheese, at room temperature

Basil infused oil, optional

DIRECTIONS

Process first six ingredients in a blender until smooth.

Add basil and mix quickly.

Let rest for 30 minutes.

Lightly oil a crepe pan and place over medium heat.

Pour $^{1}/_{4}$ cup of batter in the pan and tilt until the surface is evenly coated—work quickly!

Cook for about 1 minute or until the surface looks dry.

Lift the crepe around the edges and turn over for a quick 30 seconds to cook the flip side.

Repeat until batter is used up.

Spread finished crepes with goat cheese.

Roll up from one side.

You can put the filled crepes in a 200 degree oven to warm through, if desired.

Arrange two or three crepes on a plate, drizzle with basil infused oil and serve.

Yields 12 8" crepes

Note: Crepes can be made ahead and reheated. It's a good idea to put waxed paper in between crepes if they're being stored.

Serving Suggestions:

Slice rolled crepes into hors d'oeuvres size pieces.

Dollop cheese and layer with grilled peppers; roll and drizzle with red pepper coulis and drops of basil pesto.

Fill with grilled zucchini and oven roasted tomatoes in addition to the goat cheese.

BLUEBERRY BRUNCH BRAID

Whether you make the dough from scratch or use a shortcut from the market, this braid will be delicious and stunning on any brunch table!

INGREDIENTS

2 packages crescent roll dough (8 oz size)

8 ounces dried blueberries

$3/_4$ cup warm water

$1/_3$ cup sugar

$1/_2$ tsp cinnamon

6 ounces fresh goat cheese

3 Tbsp sugar

1 egg

1 egg for egg wash, optional

DIRECTIONS

Preheat oven to 350 degrees.

Soak berries in water until softened (about 15 minutes).

Drain excess water and combine berries with 1/3 cup sugar and cinnamon.

On jelly roll pan lined with parchment paper, roll out the crescents lightly before laying them out with the short side of triangle in center – half of the points facing right and half to the left. (see diagram)

In mixing bowl, combine the goat cheese, 3 Tbsp sugar and egg until smooth.

Spread cheese in center of dough.

Sprinkle the berries over the cheese and 'braid' up the dough by bringing the points across to the opposite side, alternating sides.

For a glossy surface, use the optional egg wash (one egg beaten and brushed on top of braid) before baking.

Bake braid for 25 minutes or until dough is golden brown.

Serve immediately.

Yields 8-10 servings

For an alternative, substitute dried apricots and omit the cinnamon.

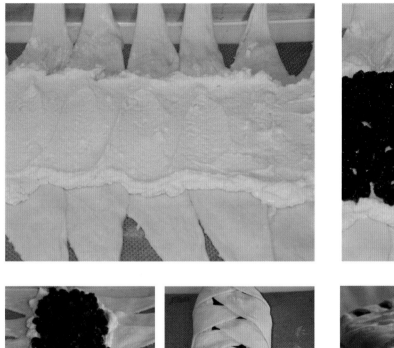

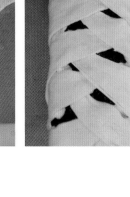

GARDEN GRILLADE WITH CREAMY PASTA

I greedily scoop up what's beautiful from the garden and grill it up . . . and dinner transports me to Lucca, Italy!

INGREDIENTS

1 zucchini

1 yellow squash

1 small, firm eggplant

3-4 Roma tomatoes

1 onion

olive oil for grilling

4-6 garlic cloves

black olives, pitted and chopped

1 pound pasta—orechiette or penne

4-6 ounces fresh goat cheese

DIRECTIONS

Preheat grill to medium-high.

Mince garlic and sauté in olive oil until just fragrant and set aside.

Wash and trim zucchini, squash and eggplant and cut $1/4$"- $1/2$" thick slices on the diagonal and brush with olive oil.

Slice tomatoes in half and brush cut side with oil.

Quarter peeled onion and brush surface with remaining oil.

Grill oiled vegetables for 5-15 minutes until they reach desired tenderness.

In the meantime, cook pasta in a large pot of salted water until desired tenderness.

Drain well, reserving $1/3$ cup water and return pasta to pot.

Take half the goat cheese and whisk with pasta water. Toss liquefied goat cheese into pasta. Add grilled vegetables, olives, garlic and toss thoroughly.

Add remaining cheese in small crumbled additions.

Season to taste with salt & pepper.

Yields 6-8 servings

Note: Rainy day option—don't want to stand out in the rain and grill? Chop all vegetables and sauté in garlic infused olive oil until done and toss with all other ingredients as above

SYLVIANNE'S POIRES FARCIES

Serve these on a bed of greens as a first course or use as a side dish.

INGREDIENTS

2-3 leeks, washed thoroughly

1 clove garlic, minced

1 tsp ginger, minced

4 pears, peeled and halved

8 ounces fresh goat cheese

olive oil

DIRECTIONS

Preheat oven to 350 degrees.

Chop leeks finely.

Sauté leek with garlic and ginger in olive oil until softened and just before they turn golden.

In a lightly oiled casserole dish, place pear halves cut side up.

Fill center with goat cheese and top with leek mixture.

Bake in oven for 10-20 minutes, until pears are softened and warm throughout.

Yields 8 servings

DESSERT PIZZA

The unexpected format belies the most wonderful combination of subtle flavors for a delicious finish to your meal.

INGREDIENTS

Pizza dough*

8-10 ounces fresh goat cheese

3 Tbsp powdered sugar, plus 2 Tbsp more for finishing

3 ounces slivered almonds

1 pint fresh raspberries

DIRECTIONS

Preheat oven to 400 degrees.

In mixing bowl, cream goat cheese and powdered sugar.

Prepared pizza dough and roll out to about 10" in diameter on either pizza stone or baking sheet.

Spread goat cheese over dough.

Top with evenly distributed berries and sprinkle almonds liberally over top.

Place on lowest oven shelf and bake until cheese is softened and before almonds get too brown, approximately 20 minutes.

Cool and slice.

*See Spring Pizza with Fresh Arugula recipe for homemade dough recipe or purchase fresh pre-prepared dough.

Yields 8 servings

CONCORD GRAPE & GOAT CHEESE CHEESECAKE

Robert Weland, Executive Chef, Poste Moderne Brasserie, Washington, DC

INGREDIENTS

2 cups cold unsalted butter, cubed

3 cups plus 6 Tbsp sugar

4 cups flour

Pinch salt

12 Tbsp melted butter

20 cups fresh Concord grapes, plus more for garnish

4 cups water

4 cups organic heavy cream

24 ounces Rainbeau Ridge fresh goat cheese

24 ounces cream cheese

8 organic eggs

4 vanilla beans, pulp only

8 Tbsp simple syrup, optional

DIRECTIONS

CRUST

Preheat oven to 350 degrees and prepare a baking sheet with parchment paper.

Cream the cubed butter and 1 cup of the sugar until smooth.

Add the flour, salt and mix until combined.

Roll the dough ¼" thick, cover and refrigerate one hour.

Remove chilled dough from refrigerator, place on baking sheet and bake until golden.

Bake until golden, about 15 minutes.

Let cool, then finely crumble into bowl.

Add the melted butter and 6 Tbsp sugar and mix.

Line a 9x9" pan with foil extending over the edge of the pan.

Press crust mixture onto the bottom of the pan.

GRAPE JUICE

Simmer 20 cups of the grapes and the water for 30 minutes.

Strain, pressing the grapes, keeping the liquid and discarding the skins and seeds.

Return to heat and cook 20 minutes, until reduced to 4 cups.

CHEESECAKE

Preheat oven to 325 degrees and prepare a large baking dish to hold the 9x9" pan and a water bath.

Bring cream and remaining 2 cups of sugar to a boil.

Simmer 15 minutes until reduced to 3 cups.

Remove from heat and cool slightly.

Using a mixer, cream the goat cheese and the cream cheese.

Add the sweetened cream, then add eggs and mix until smooth.

Place 1/2 of the mix in a separate bowl and mix in vanilla pulp.

Add 2 cups of the grape juice to the remaining batter and mix; set aside rest of grape juice for drizzling onto finished cake.

Spread the grape batter into the pan and refrigerate for 30 minutes to firm slightly.

Spread the vanilla batter on top of the chilled grape batter.

Place pan in a water bath and bake for about 45 minutes, until set.

Refrigerate overnight.

To Serve:

Lift cheesecake out of pan and cut into 2 1/2" square pieces.

Spoon reserved grape juice over the cake and around the plate.

Serving Suggestions:

Peel the skins from remaining grapes, cut in half and remove seeds, then toss with simple syrup and garnish the cake.

Add a scoop of grape sorbet on the side.

Note: You can buy prepared cookies to make into the crust by crushing and then mixing with the melted butter and pressing into the pan.

The dairy inspectors say I can't call it 'gelato' or ice cream or even a frozen dessert—they say it's a "quissentially frozen dessert"—I call it delicious!!!

INGREDIENTS

1 gallon of goat milk

$\frac{1}{2}$ cup instant espresso powder

4 Tbsp cornstarch

$1\frac{1}{2}$ cups sugar

   Optional: chocolate chips, nuts

DIRECTIONS

Warm 1 cup of milk and mix with espresso powder to dissolve.

Mix another cup of milk with corn starch to dissolve.

In a saucepan, warm the remaining milk and sugar, bringing just to a boil and stirring until the sugar is dissolved.

Stir cornstarch and milk mixture into saucepan and let simmer.

Whisk constantly and let simmer for two minutes.

Combine with espresso mixture and let cool.

Put into refrigerator and then freeze in ice cream maker according to manufacturer's instructions.

Add optional mix-ins about five minutes before the freezing process is complete.

Yields 16 servings

PEACHES WITH FRESH GOAT CURDS & SPICED ALMONDS

Michael Anthony, Executive Chef, Gramercy Tavern, New York, NY

GRAMERCY
TAVERN

INGREDIENTS
8 peaches

3 Tbsp Linden honey

$2/3$ cup Rainbeau Ridge fresh goat cheese

Spiced almond mixture:

$1/2$ cup almonds

$1/2$ cup pistachios

$1/2$ cup hazelnuts

$1/4$ cup coriander, whole

3 Tbsp sesame seeds

1 Tbsp cumin

1 tsp black peppercorns

1 Tbsp fennel seed

1 tsp salt

DIRECTIONS
Cut each peach in half and remove the pit.

Spread 2 teaspoons of goat cheese on top of each peach half.

To make the spice mixture, toast the nuts and spices together in a dry pan
    until aromatic.

Using a mortar and pestle, grind the toasted spices to create a coarse,
    sandy textured mix.

Sprinkle spice mixture over the cheese.

Drizzle with honey.

Yields 8 servings

THE MILK DEBATE

I WANT MY CHEESES TO be consistently inconsistent. I want them to be recognizable within a certain bandwidth of taste and texture, and I also want the consumer to savor the seasonal differences, like the richness of spring milk and the grassiness of summer's. As the composition of the does' milk (in terms of fat, protein and sugar) changes over the course of the milking period, yield and taste change too. Pasteurization blurs these subtleties, presenting the risk of removing and homogenizing flavor. But raw milk cheese aged less than sixty days cannot be sold to the public in the United States.

In this country, a cheesemaker has two choices: she can pasteurize the milk she uses or she can age the cheese for a minimum of 60 days, because aging will eliminate the (small) risk of harmful organisms in the cheese. In a few states, raw milk can be bought directly from a farm but not from a retail market. In these states people have tried inventive schemes, such as buying a "share" of a farm animal for their personal use of the milk, but this approach has also been challenged.

Currently I must pasteurize but I am not afraid of raw milk cheeses and I think they do taste more subtle and alive. They are inherently more interesting. Also, pasteurizing is involved and time-consuming. It means raising the temperature of the milk to a prescribed level for a certain amount of time and then cooling it down so that beneficial organisms that make cheese can be introduced again. We kill off all organisms, beneficial or not, and then have to re-introduce the bacteria in the form of cultures.

The USDA pasteurization requirements favor the need for standardization in large, industrialized cheesemaking, rather than my interest in subtle, seasonal differences in taste, varying butterfat content, etc.

The USDA procedure, which mandates pasteurization, is administered in New York by the Agriculture and Markets Department. To be inspected and approved for retail sale, our whole operation and cheese house had to conform to a phonebook-sized document of burdensome ordinances that dictate plant design, materials, equipment and process. It would put you to sleep. And each new product must be walked through this paperwork and inspection. It's not as simple as just deciding to make goat milk yogurt for sale.

The other alternative, keeping cheese sixty days, has its drawbacks as well. It means tying up capital for at least sixty days before sale. The cheesemaker needs a space with the proper temperature and humidity to store the cheeses. She must turn the cheeses for full flavor development and supervise them daily to prevent spoilage. The goal in both cases is to convert milk to cheese by the aid of microorganisms. This process can begin by itself under raw milk conditions and often with the help of added beneficial organisms in the case of pasteurized milk.

While it's true that raw milk can carry some undesirable micro-organisms as a result of unsanitary practices, many incidents of contamination of cheese are reported to happen after pasteurization. Small producers who monitor closely their herds and the conditions under which they are kept are probably in the best position to produce good, clean milk. The tradition of raw milk cheese is well established in many countries where pasteurization is not required. Many people feel that raw milk cheese is superior in taste and health benefits alike.

GOAT MILK

Goat milk is more commonly available and drunk in most of the rest of the world outside the United States. Goat and cow milk are more or less interchangeable in many farmstead cheesemaking recipes (I know some people have been successful making goat milk mozzarella, but I just haven't been able to stretch the curd into the taffy-like strands necessary for it), although some cheeses are, of course, traditionally made with certain milk, especially if they are protected by a regulated, regional definition.

It seems that some people can better tolerate goat milk than cow milk although there is a range of scientific conclusions that doesn't reveal the whole story of exactly why. Goat milk is "naturally" homogenized; that is, the fat globules are smaller and evenly dispersed in the milk. No cream separates in goat milk and the butterfat content of goat milk is lower overall although the milk of different breeds and even different herds may vary in butterfat levels. It is also high in calcium and vitamin-A. Goat milk is reported to contain more of the essential fatty acids linoleic and arachnodonic acids, in addition to a higher proportion of short-chain triglycerides (capric, caproic and caprylic acid). These short-chain and medium-chain fatty acids may be easier for intestinal enzymes to digest. There's anecdotal evidence too that some people with allergic reactions to cow milk can tolerate goat milk instead. ❖

My bottom line is consumer choice. Look for raw milk cheeses and find out what's happening in the agriculture department of your own state so you can advocate for the availability of small-production, lovingly handmade cheese.

HOMEMADE YOGURT

WE'VE COME TO THINK OF heavily sweetened, granola-topped commercial yogurt as convenience food or of the "skinny" version as diet food, but dense, whole milk yogurt with honey and walnuts is a classic Greek dessert. Even plain, my delicate doe milk yogurt can make me swoon. On a summer day, a sweet-tart bowlful with berries makes a cool yet satisfying breakfast.

Sure, it's easy to buy a cup or quart of plain yogurt but it's also fun and instructive to try making it yourself. Making quality yogurt at home will give you a feeling for cheesemaking, as well as the obvious satisfaction of doing it yourself (and saving money).

The principal is to heat milk to between 180 and 200 degrees Fahrenheit, then cool it quickly down to about 110 to 120 degrees (I have found 190 brought down to 110 works best), add some yogurt to start the lactobacilli culturing and then keep it all warm for no less than four hours so the culture can grow. Voilà. Of course, a commercial yogurt maker will keep the individual cups at just the right temperature, but you can easily rig a "warming box" from a Styrofoam box or a picnic cooler into which you can put quart glass jars. Some people pad the jars with newspapers or towels but that's not necessary. A heating pad on the bottom of such a box will work or even on the kitchen counter if the jars are also left swaddled in a towel or blanket. Even the inside of an unlit oven is cozy enough. Some people prefer a water bath set-up in a large pot or cooler, keeping the water temperature at about 100 degrees. A thermos does a great job too but holds less yogurt, and while I haven't

For Greek-Bulgarian style yogurt, simply drain the finished yogurt for a few hours in a cheesecloth-lined sieve over a bowl. If you like very thick yogurt, you can also experiment with adding some gelatin to your mix when the yogurt culture goes in. To my taste, my goat milk yogurt is ready to eat as is.

tried it, I'd bet that a crockpot set on low would provide enough heat too.

Besides this consistently warm place and the glass jars, you'll need a cooking thermometer to test that you've reached the temperatures required. A double boiler is also nice because you're less likely to boil the milk but that is not absolutely necessary.

Begin with a quart of pasteurized (not ultrapasteurized) milk: cow—yes—goat, sheep, horse or yak. Whole, skim, even reconstituted dry milk, will work. In fact, to develop a thicker yogurt, I add two to four tablespoons of dry milk powder. You can add some sweetener such as honey or sugar up front if you like, or wait until the yogurt has set. One method is to heat the milk carefully to roughly 185 degrees and hold it at that not-yet-simmering temperature just a few minutes. I usually just take the milk to 190—the milk will just ruffle up around the edge—and then turn off the heat entirely. Let it cool to 110 degrees. You can put the top part of the double boiler into an ice bath to speed that up but be careful not to cool the milk down too far.

Now pour out about three-fourths of a cup of that milk and mix it with a quarter-cup store-bought plain yogurt, which is your starter culture. The next time you can use some saved portion of your own yogurt as the starter. Mix the milk-yogurt mix back into your original warm quart. Fill your containers and nestle them into their warm place. The yogurt can take between four and twelve hours to grow and firm up. You'll have to try out your contraption to see how long. I've never had success in less than eight hours, so if I make the yogurt in the evening, it's ready to eat in the morning.

You can add fruit, jam, honey, maple syrup or other flavorings now. Those summer blueberries or sliced peaches, the applesauce you cooked down in the fall, the poached spring rhubarb? What a combination! ❖

MAKING CHEESE AT HOME

IT ISN'T TERRIBLY HARD TO try making cheese in your own kitchen. If you've experimented with bread making or beer making at home, you've got the idea of working with growing yeast or fermentation already. You'll need a couple of easy-to-mail-order supplies, a thermometer and one heavy pot at the least. Ladles, strainers, a few cheese molds and cheesecloth are helpful too.

To begin with, get some milk. Work with just a gallon the first few times. Supermarket lower fat or whole milk will work but avoid ultrapasteurized and dry milk. If you are confident in the source, you can decide yourself on the risk of using raw milk, if available. If you have access to fresh milk, cow or goat, (sure, sheep or buffalo too—knock yourself out), you can decide to pasteurize it yourself. The process is simply bringing milk to specific temperatures and holding it there for sufficient time.

To make cheese, the basic idea is to acidify the milk in one of several ways, to coagulate it into curds with the enzyme rennet and then to remove some or most of the liquid, or whey. Other cheeses can be made of the whey (ricotta, for instance) or it can be used as brine (for cheeses such as feta). For hard cheeses, the curd is usually cut, cooked and pressed to remove as much liquid as possible. For soft cheeses it may be just drained in several ways or ladled into molds by hand, as our chevre is. Depending on the cheese, aging can last two to three days or two to three years.

I suggest that you begin with the even simpler, spreadable fromage

blanc, made with a direct-set culture packet, available from cheesemaker supply houses, such as Ricki Carroll's New England Cheesemaking Supply Company. You can also purchase direct-set bacterial cultures for other cheeses. Note that the yield of the following recipe is more than two pounds of cheese.

Warm the one gallon of milk in a large pot to 180 degrees Fahrenheit and then cool it to 72 degrees. Setting up a double-boiler effect by placing the pot in a larger bowl or pan of water on the stove will protect the milk from burning. Sprinkle and mix the direct-set culture into the milk. Cover and keep warm for about twelve hours. (See One Step Yogurt.)

Then, line a colander with several layers of fine cheesecloth and ladle in the fromage blanc curd. Drain at room temperature for six to twelve hours, depending on the consistency you like. Then you can mix in salt, herbs, lemon peel, cranberries, etc. Scrape into a container and refrigerate.

With more confidence you can go on to start a mesophilic (it likes room temperature) mother culture to make cheeses such as chevre, feta, Gouda and so on. Soon you'll get the logic and knack of the steps, expand your repertoire, accumulate a little more equipment and develop a favorite. Then you might think about getting a pair of goats... ❖

Because there are so many cheeses, I suggest you use a solid recipe guide, such as my first teacher Ricki Carroll's classic cheesemaking book, *Cheesemaking Made Easy* (Storey Books, 1996), *Home Cheesemaking* (2002) or one of her several spinoffs.

FALL

BITTERSWEET
BOUNTY

A last batch of green tomato relish, a last yellow squash or cucumber cut off the vine before I pull the mildewed stalks out and finally I'm wistfully eating a last piece of MontVivant on top of a last salad. I'll have to wait another nine months before I can taste the wonderful flavor of fresh tomatoes again. But I notice I'm no longer trying to squeeze out the very last bit of milk from the goats or cheese from the milk. That's a sign as sure as the first yellow and red leaves falling from the maple trees that I'm looking forward to the end of the milking and cheesemaking season. In the summer, it's painful to lose milk. Cats may be happy but if a doe kicks over a bucket, I do cry over spilled milk. Now I watch the natural, daily decline in production with some relief. On one hand, I'm grateful and ready for a break. On the other hand, when the euphoria of being done with the relentless routine has passed, I know I'll miss it.

AS WITH SPRING, AUTUMN BRINGS a lot of change to Rainbeau Ridge. When the (human) kids head back to school after Labor Day, they are still wearing shorts and looking for a place to swim in the afternoon since the town pool is closed. But by Thanksgiving, even fleece jackets won't keep them warm enough. I might be sweltering at 92 degrees on Labor Day but within five weeks, I might wake up to an early frost. If the tender crops are stopped cold, Isaac and I might be scrambling to stretch the last of them for CAP shoppers. Late tomatoes might have to ripen off the vine. We are rescuing and saving seeds for the next season while we are also pushing to get a few hardy seeds planted to winter over.

The beds under the hoop houses are our last holdout against changing weather, and also will give us a jump on next spring with mache, lovage, claytonia, garlic and onions. Soon we'll put the unprotected beds to bed by fortifying and tidying the soil. Eventually the first hard frost arrives and my heart sinks a little. Cold weather plucks at our sleeve, sometimes bringing heavy snow before Thanksgiving and foreshadowing that long season of ice on the water buckets.

In autumn, I covet each and every fruit the plants want to give us. I revel in the bounty while at the same time, I can feel its end approaching. Before I know it, it may be too late to harvest more tomatoes or make ample sauce to get us through the winter. Until all things finally fade in the garden, I savor the joy of eating from our own backyard, regret plants we let slip through our fingers and cherish the tastes, thankful for the season we had.

Peppers
$3/pound

Mini
Sweet Bell Peppers
$2/pint
*these are GREAT
stuffed with goat cheese!

all
Beans
$3/pound

Beets
$3/bunch

Scarlet Queen
Turnips
5/$2

Hakurei
Turnips
5/$2

My customers are also sad to see the season over. At about this time, one CAP customer will comment, "I can't believe this is the last cheese." A couple of autumns ago, when I warned Chef Adam Kaye of Blue Hill at Stone Barns Center for Agriculture that our season was coming to an end, he kindly said, "Each week's delivery is a gift, as far as I'm concerned." And Joe DiMauro will have to explain to his customers that they'll have to wait until April again for our cheese.

At home, I make sure to squirrel away some cheese for the winter. I freeze fresh, unsalted curd for winter recipes and I float the smaller cheese rounds in olive oil and herbs. Then I'll be able to reach smugly into the freezer or fridge in the winter and remember the tastes of summer. This is also the season when I experiment again with hard cheeses, which could be aged over the winter and allow me to have a more continuous offering.

Customers come in looking for Lisa's cheese and our weekly allocation always sells out fast. In November I have to warn store customers that the season will be over soon and in the spring, I put a sign that tells them it's coming back. They look for the Rainbeau Ridge and if we sell out, they ask, "Where's the cheese?" We hate having to take Rainbeau Ridge cheese off the menu at the restaurant in the late fall too.

I love Lisa's concept and her energy. She's a summer breeze and sometimes a whirlwind. Her farm is a great place and you can see how she knows and cares for her animals. Lisa is as passionate about her cheese and her customers as I am about fish. I wanted to be a pioneer in carrying her stuff because local products were part of my expansion plan for the new store. Now I count on her and she counts on me.

—Joe DiMauro

If fall is bitter, it's also sweet, bracing and invigorating. While the children are sharpening pencils, shaking sand out of their towels and lacing up soccer cleats, we adults file the summer snapshots, start raking leaves and get back to work. The trees flame with brilliant color and I start thinking about turtleneck sweaters and fires in the fireplace while daily salads are being replaced by daily soups. I have a schizophrenic palate that wants those last tomato sandwiches right now but also has a hankering for a first Italian blue plum tart or a warm apple crisp.

As the weather cools, we gather yet another crop of lettuce, arugula and brassicas, such as cabbage and broccoli, yielding plenty of greens. Small potatoes, purple turnips and heavy orange squash are welcomed in too. Abundance fills our kitchens and our mouths. Just when I'm a little tomato-fatigued and on zucchini overload, I can start riffing on pumpkin in my cooking and serve Seckel pears, or apples from the small orchard we are restoring on the farm, with slices of Meridian.

Knowing this ripeness and plenty won't last forever, I rifle through my recipes for ways to put by for winter. Outside, the crisp air smells

of wood smoke and apples. Inside, my kitchen is filled with the aromas (and spatters) of raspberry jam, simmered from those jewel-like berries from a neighboring farm, and the tomato and basil sauce I made to freeze for the winter. If I'm lucky, I'll have enough tomatoes so that I won't have to choose between chili and barbecue sauce for the rest, and I'll have enough pears to both can them with ginger and cook up a batch of sweet-tart, curried pear chutney.

WRAPPING UP

Eventually, one morning after the clocks "fall back," a good rainstorm will knock the few remaining brown leaves off the trees. The mornings will have become greyer and the midday light weaker. It's then, when I'm almost too exhausted to think about it, that I face my old-fashioned, black-and-white composition book with those "should have" thoughts. What went well this season and what will I change in the next? I see that with the herd's steady growth, there are new issues to consider, such as the cost-effective limits of the herd, the size of the milking parlor, the plant capacity of our cheese house equipment, our staffing needs and how to move the "extra" kids off the farm more quickly. While, with many seasons behind me, the cheese house operation is working more smoothly than ever, I can't help but cringe when I remember that sixty kids on the ground by April 15 was a nightmare.

Breeding the does is the final task on the far end of fall's arc. Inevitably, the responsibility of another year on the farm hits me. I am committing to farm life for another round. Still, I already feel eager to see the offspring my pairings will produce next year. My three or four bucks get antsy as early as July or August, spraying themselves with urine, crashing against each other or banging at the fences. Their musky smell is pervasive throughout the farm when it's breezy. By the end of the day, I might not notice it so much but when I come at night, Mark does. I reek just from working nearby.

The shorter days and weaker light mean that the veteran does and

the sturdy 60- to 70-pound yearlings are beginning to come into heat, a condition I learned to recognize much more easily than the onset of their labors! They are vocalizing, pacing the fence line and twitching their tails. In my small herd, Ron and I time the matings to be sure the does will kid when it's warm enough and manage them to keep track of who breeds with whom. Beginning in late October, I stagger their breeding but try to have it all done by Thanksgiving, with a couple of stragglers in early December. It's exciting to be growing my herd but this is another point in the year when tough "real farmer" decisions must be made. I have to cull the herd either because I have too many bucks to feed through the winter or because a doe has some feature that, for example, makes milking her too inefficient. After a last desperate effort to find homes for them, I send them off to sure slaughter. At least I can imagine the new season beginning in the does' growing bellies and I'm grateful that this year's cycle is nearly over.

The does' milk production naturally diminishes and I gradually milk them less and less to move them towards drying off. Around early November, I might still be milking twice a day, but making cheese perhaps only every other day because there is that much less milk. The does need some rest too, at least two non-producing months in order to carry their pregnancies to term in good condition.

Fall reduces the scale of production but my elbows and shoulders ache and my hands and feet crack with dryness from the growing cold. By early November, I reach for my heavier grey gloves and add a layer of long underwear at both evening and early milkings. I know in my heart that it's time for time off.

RE-FOCUS

The cheese house and the garden may be settling in for the winter sleep but other programs, such as In Lisa's Kitchen, come into sharp focus. Trained chef and writer, Nicki Sizemore has allowed us to expand the cooking series beyond what I was able to do alone. She both organizes and teaches. Crowding around the cooking island in the farmhouse kitchen, we watch the inspired chefs in our cooking-demo series. The harvest bounty at the farm provides them a soapbox to preach farm-to-table connections. We bring in talented local food personalities to teach about seasonal ingredients and menus, breads, tarts and preserves. Jeff Raider, executive chef of Lincoln Center's restaurants, takes a stroll in the garden and shows us how to improvise recipes from the freshest goodies we stumble upon there. Participants ask questions, share possibilities and make suggestions. Renowned chef Phil McGrath might lead a session on the delights of farm eggs or on Thanksgiving side dishes.

In the sessions I lead myself, I love sharing, as I always have, some of the goat cheese recipes you'll find in this book, as well as what I've learned on the farm about moving incrementally towards seasonal and balanced eating and living. I look forward to sitting down to eat with others around the large table.

The children in the Sprouts after-school program learn to put by and preserve for winter too. Saving, using everything and not wasting, becomes part of their routine. When they cook up our apples, they understand easily what real food is. Applesauce has three ingredients, all of which they can pronounce. They are also making pickles,

My boys have learned so much, from how to feed chickens to how to weed a garden. My five year-old Hale cooks now and is obsessed with animals. He wants his own farm and he promises to feed the chickens. My two year-old Henry is fearless; he practically herds the sheep. Now they both say cucumbers are "awesome" and ask to make pickles at home. They know that maple syrup must come from trees, not plastic bottles, and that apples don't grow with stickers on them. I can't imagine finding another place where there are so many different ways to start good habits that will influence the boys for a lifetime.

The cooking demos are my relaxing, secret indulgence and I always learn something new! In fact, I come away from all the farm programs ready to make some small change that resonates for me. The gentle nudge towards more sustainable living is integrated so smoothly and warmly that it just envelopes you. Even straight beginners can always ask questions.

—Whitney Brown

pumpkin bars, ketchup and apple bread pudding. In the fall, we stress how all parts of the farm get ready for winter, naming this session by its themes: Preserving, Preparing, Protecting.

The children discover that the goats' sleek, smooth coats go as furry as those of teddy bears. They help put the garden to bed and fill up bird feeders. We talk about migration, hibernation, adaptation and how to help domesticated animals with bedding, shelter, and windbreaks. Parents like Whitney Brown see how this kind of learning on the farm has influenced her children.

We reach out to the greater public locally with our spring sheep shearing, the summer Open Farm Days and Tomato Jamboree and in the fall, the Fall Fest. This autumn event celebrates the last flush of the garden and invites our surrounding community onto the farm. It has grown from one hundred to four hundred attendees in three years. Everyone helps out—staff, spouses, volunteers, my nephews' band, even my dad and brother—in the crafts, old-fashioned games and garlic planting. The festival always makes me think about the carnival that my childhood neighbor and I ran in our backyard when we were eleven years old. It's good, clean, do-it-yourself fun.

In late fall, we celebrate the wide possibilities of the harvest but also face its end. Milking and cheese taper off and I take on the responsibilities of breeding. In the garden and the kitchen, we emulate the Ant rather than the Grasshopper by tidying up and storing up for the coming winter. We come back inside to the rich feast of Thanksgiving, the holiday which completes the transition from summer's frenzy to winter's peace.

The rich colors of autumn's backdrop, the breath-taking, Northeast spectacle of turning leaves, show up in the kitchen too, along with comforting, hearty flavors. The recipes in this section combine our cheese with deep orange pumpkin, ruddy red apples and warm brown potatoes, among other ingredients. You'll find some from our family's eclectic Thanksgiving menu, which gives traditional, seasonal ingredients a reinvigorating twist. There is still a proud turkey on the table—ours is regional and organic—but my mother's sweet potatoes with marshmallows, green beans, chopped liver and pigs in a blanket have been replaced by sweet potatoes gauffrette, corn fritters and a savory goat cheese cheesecake.

RONDVIVANT EN CROUTE

Need an instant dish for a spontaneous party? Add your own special combination of toppings to change this up.

INGREDIENTS

- 1 sheet of puff pastry dough, defrosted
- 8-16 ounces RondVivant
- 4 ounces cranberry chutney
- 1 egg

DIRECTIONS

Preheat oven to 450 degrees.

Roll softened puff pastry to several inches wider than the diameter of your cheese.

Place round of cheese in center of pastry dough.

Spread your favorite topping on top of goat cheese round.

Bring corners of pastry to center.

Pinch pastry or overlap pastry corners to seal up.

Alternatively, seal dough on underside and place extra dough trimmings decoratively on top. Affix dough with a little water.

Beat 1 egg and brush as egg wash over pastry.

Place in very hot oven, turn down to 350 degrees and bake for 25 minutes or until golden brown and puffed.

Serve with slices of French bread or crackers.

Yields 16+ servings

Note: As an alternative topping, use 3 ounces chopped pecans mixed with $1/2$ cup of brown sugar.

Know your cheese as heat can affect its flavor.

SWEET POTATOES GAUFRETTE

Perfect to serve on Thanksgiving—traditional ingredients with an updated twist. Topped with softened goat cheese, these 'chips' are a great start to your meal.

INGREDIENTS

2 sweet potatoes

4-6 ounces fresh goat cheese (plain or herbed)

oil for frying

Garnish Options:

pine nuts

cranberry chutney

DIRECTIONS

Peel sweet potatoes.

Using a mandoline's fluted cutting edge, cut potato in one direction; rotate the potato 90 degrees; cut again and achieve a weave effect. (You may have to adjust the thickness of your mandoline.)

Place enough oil in a fry pay to cover potatoes (about · inch) and turn on medium-high heat.

Deep fry all of the potatoes until brown, turning as necessary, and remove to drain on paper towel. (As a lower fat alternative, spray with olive oil and bake at 350 degrees for about 25 minutes).

At this point the potato gaufrettes can be stored in an airtight container for up to 2 days.

Put softened goat cheese in a piping bag and pipe a small amount on each potato slice.

Can be served as is or topped with lightly toasted pine nuts or chutney.

Yields 24 pieces

FALL CIDER CHOPPED SALAD

Johnny Holzworth, Executive Chef, The Dressing Room, Westport, CT

VINAIGRETTE

INGREDIENTS

1 quart fresh apple cider

1 tsp red wine vinegar, preferably reisling vinegar

1 cup grapeseed oil

pinch of salt

DIRECTIONS

Place apple cider in large saucepan and allow it to reduce to syrup
   consistency over medium low heat, skimming regularly.

Let cool.

Add vinegar, pinch of salt.

Whisk in grapeseed oil.

CHOPPED SALAD

INGREDIENTS

3 celery ribs, cut into $1/2$ inch dice

6 baby multi-colored carrots peeled, blanched and cut into $1/2$ inch dice

2 local heirloom apples, cored and diced

$1/2$ cucumber peeled, seeded and diced

1 cup chicory, chopped

1 cup red endive, chopped

$1/2$ cup of picked mixed herbs, including parsley, chervil, tarragon

salt & pepper to taste

$1/4$ cup toasted almond slivers

$1/2$ cup crumbled Rainbeau Ridge fresh goat cheese

Yields 6 servings

Assembly:

In a large bowl, mix all chopped salad ingredients, except the goat cheese and almonds.

Add the vinaigrette.

Toss and adjust with salt and pepper.

Divide salad among six plates.

Top with goat cheese and toasted almonds.

SAVORY CHEVRE CHEESECAKE

Philip McGrath, Chef/Owner, Iron Horse Grill, Pleasantville, NY

INGREDIENTS

For the crust:

3/4 cup breadcrumbs

1/2 cup finely chopped walnuts

2 Tbsp olive oil

coarse salt & fresh pepper to taste

For the cake:

1 lb Rainbeau Ridge fresh goat cheese, room temperature

4 egg yolks

4 oz heavy cream

1 tsp chopped rosemary

grated rind of one lemon, reserve the rest for beets

coarse salt & fresh pepper to taste

sliced beets, optimal when serving

DIRECTIONS

Preheat the oven to 350 degrees.

For the crust, combine all ingredients and mix well.

Next, cream the cheese in a mixing bowl.

Add the yolks one at a time, then add the cream, rosemary and lemon rind.

Season with salt and pepper.

Line the bottom of an 8" spring form pan or individual ramekins with the crust mix and press firmly.

Add the cheese mixture and bake in a water bath in the oven until set, about 1 hour for a large cake or 45 minutes for the ramekins.

Let cool completely.

Remove from pan and serve with sliced beets brushed with olive oil and a squeeze of the reserved lemon.

Yields 6 servings

HEIRLOOM TOMATO & GOAT CHEESE TART

Lauren Braun Costello, Chef/Author, *The Competent Cook*

INGREDIENTS

For the tomato jam:

2 pints grape or cherry tomatoes

6 whole shallots, peeled

4 cloves garlic, peeled

4 sprigs thyme

olive oil

salt & pepper to taste

For the tart:

1 sheet puff pastry (if frozen, defrost according to label)

1 cup tomato jam

6 ounces Rainbeau Ridge fresh goat cheese, crumbled

1 pint small heirloom tomatoes, halved or quartered

freshly ground black pepper

extra virgin olive oil

coarse sea salt

fresh basil leaves

DIRECTIONS

Preheat the oven to 400 degrees.

To make the tomato jam, combine the tomatoes, shallots, garlic, and thyme in a rimmed baking sheet pan.

Drizzle with olive oil, and sprinkle generously with salt and pepper.

Roast for 20-30 minutes, or until the shallots have caramelized and softened.

Remove the pan from the oven and transfer the tomato mixture to a food processor.

Puree for several seconds until more or less smooth.

Allow to cool before assembling the tart.

To make the tart, line a baking sheet with parchment paper.

Place the puff pastry on the baking sheet, then spread the tomato jam
evenly over the surface, leaving a $1/2$-inch border.

Sprinkle with the crumbled goat cheese.

Place the tomato pieces evenly on top.

Top with freshly ground black pepper and bake in the oven for 30 minutes,
or until the edges of the pastry are golden brown and have puffed.

Remove from the oven, drizzle lightly with extra virgin olive oil, season with
finishing salt, and sprinkle with whole fresh basil leaves.

Cut into pieces to serve warm or at room temperature.

Yields 24 pieces

Note: The tomato jam may be made up to one week in advance and stored in
an airtight container in the refrigerator.

POTATOES & LEEKS

Peasant food by anyone's account, this was typical of lunch at the ferme in Poummoue. It is simple and delicious.

INGREDIENTS

6 Russet potatoes, sliced very thin

3 medium leeks, white and pale green part only, sliced finely

3 tbsp olive oil

1 Tbsp fresh thyme, finely chopped

1 Tbsp fresh oregano, finely chopped

4-6 ounces fresh goat cheese

salt & pepper to taste

DIRECTIONS

Preheat oven to 350 degrees.

Lightly oil a 9x9 glass baking dish.

In heavy skillet, heat oil over medium heat.

Add leeks and sauté until tender about 15 minutes.

Add herbs and cook 2 more minutes.

Season with salt & pepper.

Arrange potatoes to cover bottom of baking dish.

Cover potato layer with $1/4$ of leek mixture.

Dollup one fourth of goat cheese over leeks.

Repeat this layering 3 more times.

Cover dish with foil and bake for 25 minutes.

Uncover and bake another 10-15 until potatoes are tender.

Yields 4-6 servings

STUFFED PORTABELLA MUSHOOMS WITH THYME

The tanginess of the cheese complements the earthy taste and texture of the mushroom.

INGREDIENTS

4 large unbroken Portabella mushroom caps

12 ounces fresh goat cheese

1 Tbsp fresh thyme, or 1 tsp dried thyme

1 Tbsp balsamic vinegar

10 oz. baby spinach, arugula or other tender greens

DIRECTIONS

Preheat oven to 350 degrees.

Clean mushrooms by wiping outside with clean damp cloth.

Place skin side down on foil lined jelly roll or oven pan.

In small bowl, mix goat cheese with thyme.

Stuff mushrooms with cheese.

Drizzle balsamic vinegar over the cheese.

Bake for 15 minutes.

Serve on a bed of baby spinach, arugula or young greens.

Yields 4 servings

EGGPLANT RAGOUT BAKED POTATOES

Too often we think of baked potatoes only as a 'meal' when we're at a county fair. Lower in calories and fat and more interesting in taste, goat cheese replaces traditional sour cream and makes this healthy comfort food a great choice any time.

INGREDIENTS

2 medium eggplants, rinsed and cubed (1/2")
Kosher salt
2-4 garlic cloves, minced
1 medium onion, finely chopped
3-4 Roma tomatoes or 15-ounce can diced tomatoes, drained
1 15 ounce can chickpeas, drained
2 tsp minced fresh parsley
4 ounces fresh goat cheese
salt & pepper
4 8-10 ounce Russet potatoes, thoroughly washed and dried
olive oil
6 ounces fresh goat cheese

DIRECTIONS

For the ragout:

Dice eggplant and toss with salt in bowl.

Let stand about 10-20 minutes while you're preparing the rest.

Heat olive oil in sauté pan over medium heat.

Add onion, and sauté until softened.

Add garlic and sauté until fragrant.

Stir in tomatoes, chickpeas, and eggplant cubes (draining liquid before adding eggplant).

Reduce heat to medium-low, and cook 15 minutes, or until eggplant is tender but not mushy. Season with parsley and salt and pepper to taste.

For the potatoes:

Preheat oven to 350 degrees.

Pierce potatoes in several places with fork.

Lightly coat each potato with oil and salt.

Place potatoes directly on oven rack, with a baking pan under the rack to catch drippings.

Bake until cooked through, about 1 hour 15 minutes.

Potatoes will look slightly puffy.

Cool 5 minutes.

To assemble:

Some people like to halve the potatoes; a slightly nicer presentation is to cut an 'X' in the top and pinch the potato open before adding the topping.

Spoon heated eggplant ragout over the top and dollop on the goat cheese.

Yields 4 servings

Note: Potatoes made in advance can be returned to the oven to heat through before adding toppings.

155

PANKO-CRUSTED HALIBUT

Delicious served over a bed of orzo with seasonal vegetables.

INGREDIENTS

4 halibut filets, each $1/2$ pound

2 cups panko (Japanese bread crumbs)

4 ounces firm, ChevreLog, grated

4 Tbsp flour

2 eggs

olive oil

juice of half a lemon

DIRECTIONS

Preheat oven to 350 degrees.

Beat eggs and put in shallow glass dish.

Mix cheese with panko.

Dust top side of fish with flour, then dip into egg wash and then coat fish top with cheese and panko mixture.

Coat another glass baking dish lightly with oil.

Gently place fish, crusted side up, into baking dish.

Squeeze lemon juice on top of fish pieces and bake for about 20-25 minutes, until fish is tender, being careful not to overcook.

Serve hot, straight from the oven.

Yields 4 servings

STUFFED CHICKEN BREASTS

The presentation matches the wonderful taste by slicing the baked breast on the diagonal for plating.

INGREDIENTS

4 ounces fresh goat cheese

$1/4$ cup fresh basil, chiffonade*

$1/4$ cup pitted Kalamata olives, chopped

$1/4$ cup sun-dried tomatoes, chopped

4 chicken breast halves, skinless and boneless

2 tsp extra virgin olive oil

DIRECTIONS

Preheat oven to 400 degrees.

In a small bowl, combine goat cheese, basil, olives and tomatoes.

Pound chicken breasts between two pieces of waxed paper until thin.

Spoon equal portions of the goat cheese mixture onto each flattened chicken breast.

Roll the chicken breasts (from the short end) and secure with a toothpick.

They may be refrigerated at this point up to 4 hours ahead of use.

Heat a large skillet over medium heat.

Add the oil to coat the bottom completely.

Season chicken breasts with salt and pepper.

Place chicken breasts seam side down in pan.

Cook over medium-high heat for 4 to 5 minutes, until chicken is browned. Use tongs to carefully turn chicken over, then transfer chicken to glass pan and into the oven.

Bake for 20 to 25 minutes, until chicken is cooked through.

To serve, slice chicken on the bias and spread slices to fan out or split into two halves and overlap.

Place chicken over a bed of lightly dressed greens.

Yields 4 servings

* Chiffonade—Wash and dry basil. Stack individual leaves and roll bunch from end to end. Turn 90 degrees and slice from open end to opposite end. Holding the bunch together, chop perpendicular through the slices to achieve a nice chopped basil.

TURKEY, PEAR, CRANBERRY & GOAT CHEESE RISOTTO

A great option for Thanksgiving leftover turkey, but so delicious you should make it just because!

INGREDIENTS

1 cup arborio rice

2 Tbsp light olive oil

1 onion chopped finely

3-4 garlic cloves, minced

2 cups water or vegetable or chicken stock, kept at a simmer

1 cup white wine

4 ounces fresh goat cheese

1 cup cooked turkey, diced into uniform $1/2$" pieces

1 ripe pear, cored and diced into $1/2$" pieces

$1/3$ cup dried cranberries

salt & pepper to taste

DIRECTIONS

Heat a large skillet over medium-high heat until hot.

Add olive oil.

Stir in onion and sauté until softened.

Add garlic and stir about 2 minutes.

Add rice—and continue to stir until rice begins to brown slightly.

With water (or stock), gradually add liquid a little at a time at a time, just enough to keep rice covered, stirring continuously.

As liquid is absorbed add another 1/4 cup, maintaining flame so rice is just simmering.

When liquid is absorbed, add wine and continue stirring until mixture reaches desired consistency and rice is tender.

Remove from heat and stir in goat cheese.

Fold in turkey, pear and cranberries.

Season to taste with salt & pepper.

Serve immediately.

Tips:

Keep liquids to be added to rice at a simmer so when you make additions, you are maintaining temperature.

If you want to double, use 2 cups rice and add 3 cups water or stock, keeping the 1 cup white wine quantity as is); you can vary the turkey & pear quantity easily.

Use firm 'winter' pear varieties. I like Anjou or Bosc and use the fresh if they're ripe and consider roasting the pears for enhanced flavor.

Yields 4 servings

Seasonal Variations: Risotto is so versatile. Once you have the technique down to make it the desired consistency, experiment with add-ins. For spring, try peas and fresh herbs like parcel & lovage; in summer, try rainbow colored chard that you sauté in the onions and garlic before adding the rice. Roasted tomatoes, mushrooms and roasted beets are some of my other favorite variations.

SAVORY WILD MUSHROOM TART

Randell Dodge, Chef/Owner, Red Barn Bakery, Bedford, NY

INGREDIENTS

1 sheet puff pastry (defrosted per label)

1 egg yolk

5 Tbsp extra virgin olive oil

1 1/2 cups sliced onions

1 1/2 pounds wild mushrooms, cleaned and torn into bite-size pieces

1 tsp thyme leaves

2 to 3 cloves garlic

2 Tbsp butter

1 cup sliced leeks

1/4 cup Rainbeau Ridge MontVivant

2 large eggs

1 1/2 cups cream

1 cup flat leaf parsley, minced

Pinch nutmeg

1/4 cup Rainbeau Ridge fresh goat cheese

1 tablespoon snipped chives

Optional: Roasted pine nuts or walnuts

DIRECTIONS

Preheat the oven to 400 degrees.

Unroll the puff pastry onto a baking sheet lined with parchment paper.

Score the pastry, leaving a 1/4-inch border around the edge.

Make an egg wash using 1 egg yolk and brush the egg wash around the border.

Freeze the dough until you are ready to use.

Coat a roasting pan with olive oil, add the onions and top with the mushrooms.

Drizzle with a bit more olive oil, and toss with thyme, garlic and salt and pepper to taste.

Roast in oven for 1 hour, tossing occasionally.

In a separate pan on the stove top, sauté the leeks in butter until wilted and translucent and remove from heat.

In a food processor, combine the MontVivant with 1 Tbsp of olive oil and process until smooth.

In a separate bowl, combine 2 eggs with heavy cream, parsley, salt, pepper and nutmeg.

To assemble the tart:

Remove puff pastry from freezer.

Spread the MontVivant mixture over the puff pastry (not on the border).

Arrange the sautéed leeks over the top, followed by the roasted onions and mushrooms.

Pour the egg and cream mixture over the mushrooms and onions.

Next, dot with the goat cheese and chives.

You can also sprinkle roasted nuts over the top if you wish.

Bake for 20-25 minutes until pastry puffs and browns.

Yields 12 servings

BLACK OLIVE & ROSEMARY MUFFINS

Rosemary is one of my favorite herbs to pair with goat cheese. This savory treat is perfect at brunch but is grown up enough to accompany a glass of wine.

INGREDIENTS

2 cups flour

1 Tbsp sugar

2 tsp baking powder

$1/2$ tsp baking soda

$1/2$ tsp salt

1 tsp dry mustard

1 tsp garlic powder

1 cup goat milk

$1/4$ cup olive oil

1 egg

1 6-ounce can pitted black olives, chopped

2 tsp chopped fresh rosemary

6 ounces fresh goat cheese

DIRECTIONS

Prepare muffin pan with paper liners or spray with oil (for 12 muffins).

Preheat oven to 375 degrees.

Mix dry ingredients together.

In a large bowl, whisk milk, oil, egg, chopped olives and rosemary.

Add dry ingredients and mix well.

Spoon $1/2$ of the mixture into muffin cups.

Drop a teaspoon of goat cheese in each and top off with remaining batter.

Bake for 25-30 minutes until golden brown.

Yields 12 muffins

BAKED STUFFED APPLE

Home from a day of picking? Bake these up for an after dinner treat! Although the recipe calls for Granny Smith, Winesap and Jonagold also work well.

INGREDIENTS

4 Granny Smith apples

8 ounces fresh goat cheese

$1/3$ cup currants

$1/3$ cup apple cider vinegar

$1/3$ cup chopped walnuts

DIRECTIONS

Preheat oven to 375 degrees.

Prepare glass baking dish with cooking spray or butter.

Soak currants in cider vinegar until softened.

Wash apples—they do not need to be peeled but can be.

Cut apples horizontally along the 'equator'.

Core and level rounded end to stabilize.

Place apples in the baking dish and bake for about 10 minutes, until they start to soften.

Remove from oven and stuff the apples with goat cheese and top with drained currants and walnuts.

Continue baking in oven for about 15 minutes more, just as goat cheese starts to brown.

Yields 8 Servings

DOUBLE DECKER PUMPKIN CHEESECAKE

Who could resist this twist on traditional fall ingredients?

INGREDIENTS

For the crust:

1 cup ginger snaps finely ground (about 20 cookies or 6 ounces)

3 Tbsp butter

2 Tbsp sugar

For the filling:

24 ounces fresh goat cheese

1 cup sugar

3 Tbsp flour

3 large eggs

1 Tbsp vanilla

1 tspcinnamon

1/4 tsp allspice

1/4 tsp nutmeg

1/4 cup brown sugar

1 cup pumpkin puree

DIRECTIONS

Preheat oven to 350 degrees.

Prepare 9" spring form pan, buttering sides and bottom. (You can line the bottom with parchment paper but butter that too.)

For the crust:

Crush ginger snaps in food processor until finely ground.

Add sugar and process again.

Add butter and process until just moistened.

Press mixture to form crust into bottom of prepared pan and come up slightly on the sides with any excess.

For the filling:

In mixer, beat together cheese, sugar and flour until smooth.

Add eggs, one at a time.

Add vanilla, beating on low until all ingredients are thoroughly incorporated.

Measure two generous cups and put this 'creamed' goat cheese batter aside.

In remaining batter, add final spices and sugar and pumpkin puree. Beat until smooth.

Spread the pumpkin batter gently onto the crust in the spring form pan.

Top with plain 'creamed cheese' batter.

In shallow roasting pan, set filled spring form pan and fill with hot water to 1" up the sides.

Bake at 350 degrees for 50-60 minutes until top is golden in color.

Open oven and turn off temperature and leave set one hour.

Remove pan from oven and leave on rack for 1 hour before refrigerating at least 4-6 hours.

May be kept refrigerated for up to one week.

Bring to room temperature before serving.

Yields 10-12 servings

Note: As an alternative to the two layers approach—you can put $2/3$ of pumpkin batter in pan and dollop cheese batter in random places. Top with remaining pumpkin batter and swirl through all layers with a sharp knife.

HARVEST CAKE WITH
REAL MAPLE CREAM ICING

Transitioning from winter to spring, we flirt with temperatures that dip below freezing at night and warm up to 'flip flop' weather by day. What better conditions could we ask for to tap our sugar maple trees? The sap is boiled down to make our home made maple syrup. Try it yourself. Otherwise, be sure to buy the real thing.

MAPLE ICING

INGREDIENTS

- 16 ounces fresh goat cheese
- 4 Tbsp confectioner's sugar
- $1/3$ cup pure maple syrup

DIRECTIONS

In mixer, beat cheese and sugar vigorously until creamy.

Slowly add maple syrup until combined.

Refrigerate up to 3 days.

HARVEST CAKE

INGREDIENTS

- 1 $1/2$ cups all-purpose flour
- $3/4$ cup sugar
- 2 tsp ground cinnamon
- $1/4$ tsp ground cardamom
- $1/8$ tsp nutmeg
- 1 tsp baking soda
- $1/4$ tsp salt
- $1/2$ cup Granny Smith apple, peeled and grated
- $1/2$ cup carrot, grated
- $1/2$ cup zucchini, shredded
- $1/4$ cup walnuts, chopped
- $1/4$ cup canola oil
- 2 large eggs

DIRECTIONS

Preheat oven to 375 degrees.

Prepare 2 8" loaf pans or one bundt pan lightly with oil or cooking spray.

Sift dry ingredients together.

Mix grated apples, carrots, and zucchini together in another bowl.

In a mixing bowl, beat oil and eggs thoroughly.

Add dry ingredients in 3 additions.

Gently mix in apples, carrots, and zucchini and stir in walnuts.

Pour into prepared pan(s).

Bake in oven about 30-40 minutes until toothpick comes out clean.

Cool to room temperature before icing.

Yields 16 slices

Alternative suggestions for the icing:

You won't be able to resist dipping into the icing as is—but wait! Use it as a frosting for carrot cake, pumpkin spice bread or the harvest cake suggested here.

Pipe some icing into small pastry shells and top with a blueberry for a great dessert.

Perfect as a cannoli filling, just pipe this inside!.

BEES MAKE HONEY

AT THE END OF THE SUMMER, when the frames of honeycomb in the hives are full, we lift them out of the hive and cut off the hard capping produced by the bees. Then we fit the frames into the baskets of the honey extractor. After the centrifugal force of the extractor throws the honey out of the comb, we collect the sticky, sweet-smelling honey and bottle it. A row of clean jars of honey on a cool, dry shelf is something to be proud of.

Honey is an ancient, valued and healthful sweetener. Raw honey is easy to digest, contains trace vitamins and minerals and has been shown to have germicidal, antibacterial and antiviral properties as well as anti-inflammatory, possibly healing qualities. It's also reported to be helpful in reducing allergies since it encourages the immune system against local pollens.

We first started keeping bees at Rainbeau Ridge under the expert eye of Al Carman, a knowledgeable, long-time local beekeeper. I loved watching Al in his netted hat, smoking our bees into laziness and handling them calmly and gently. He does get stung, yes, but not unduly using his gloves and other protective equipment.

With a little sensitivity to your neighbors, bees can be kept in even a suburban backyard and most common strains of bees are gentle enough to keep in a city. It's a good idea to check on any local regulations but even if space is tight, you can consider keeping a few hives in somebody's larger yard, especially if they have a few fruit trees that would benefit from those busy pollinators. Fruit and vegetable gardeners and gardening clubs might also know about possible locations, since most gardeners understand how bees fit into a food system. The bees can be purchased by mail or sometimes from another beekeeper.

With a little luck in finding used equipment, and sometimes the help of a local beekeeping club, the startup costs for backyard beekeeping are not prohibitive. There is an initial investment in hives, protective clothing, a smoker and possibly in a centrifugal honey extractor eventually.

Probably the spring is the best time to start and two colonies, or hives, is probably the minimum to start with. Bees fly as far as two or three miles when foraging for food but you want to keep them close to home so they can collect nectar more efficiently and in turn strengthen the colony. We keep one group of hives on the far side of a small apple orchard we are restoring. It's important to provide water available at the proper distance for your bees too. That also keeps them at home, healthy and foraging. Beekeeping is not terribly time-consuming but hives should be checked regularly.

The warm sweetness of honey contrasts perfectly with tangy goat cheese. At Rainbeau Ridge, our honey is the palest ginger ale gold, but honey can be as rich and dark as stout, depending on the flowers it is gathered from. The darker the color, the deeper the flavor. ❖

An active hive can have as many as thirty-five thousand bees at the height of production! An average hive will produce thirty to fifty pounds of honey a year but the yield can swing wildly from zero to a hundred pounds. Happily, worker bees gather much more than they can use for their winter storage needs and in exchange for their honey, you are giving them a good, clean home.

COMPOSTING

COMPOSTING IS JUST THE RECYCLING OF ORGANIC MATTER. You set aside plant materials in your kitchen or yard, pile them up somewhere outside where they won't get in your way . . . and wait. Eventually microbes will do their job and all that stuff will rot into soil, which you will use to grow more plants. It's that easy.

The spent plants from summer's garden, all those leaves you rake in the fall and all the vegetable trimmings: you and your family will be amazed at how much stuff you generate that can be carried out to your compost bin. Situate it far enough from your house (because of the possibility of animals or odors), but close enough to be convenient. You will not compost meat, skin or bones, dairy products, grass clipping treated with chemicals or colored paper. But, you'll see just how much your garbage load is reduced by the leaves, brown paper bags, egg cartons, plant and flower trimmings, onion skins, coffee grounds, tea leaves or bags, eggshells, orange peels and other fruit and vegetable peelings you throw in there.

You can apply more specific formulas, but basically think of layering "brown" and "green" to keep the compost cooking. Leaves, dead plant matter and cellulose (paper) are brown; they provide aeration. Eggshells, grounds, vegetable and fruit trimmings are green; they provide moisture and nitrogen. Your compost should be moist enough to keep the microbes happy, but not a soggy (and possibly smelly) mess. You can dampen the compost some to keep it rotting if it dries out in hot weather or cover the bin with a tarp if there is a period of prolonged rain and the bin has a very open design (for example, a wire mesh cage form).

Use a simple system that makes it easy for you. Collect the leavings in a large plastic container with a lid on the kitchen counter or a small, covered, galvanized bucket under the sink. When it's filled, take it out to the compost bin and empty the collection. Done. It's a fairly easy new habit to form. Compost bins can be as small as roughly three-feet square or can be taller rectangles. They can also be shaped like balls that allow you to easily mix up the compost by rolling them or tube-shapes mounted on legs that can be turned with a crank. You want a design that allows for some ventilation, seals tightly but also opens easily on top (a spring closing mechanism works nicely) and has some kind of doors or drawers on the bottom so you can get to the new dirt from underneath when you need to. The whole system should cost under a hundred dollars.

If you do have the space well away from your house, you can also fashion a roughly fenced area covered with chicken wire. At Rainbeau Ridge we use reclaimed, untreated wooden pallets that can be built up to enclose the pile as it grows. Our chickens get first crack at reducing the rich pile. Small animals may get in too, but generally won't be able to strew around the mess much. In fact their tunneling may aerate the compost.

You can throw in an occasional bucket of wood ash from your fireplace or wood stove. In addition, some sources say newspapers are fine to compost because they are increasingly printed with soy-based inks. Sawdust and wood chips are fine too, assuming you know the wood has not been chemically treated. You will also want to occasionally fork up, turn over or at least poke some holes into your compost with a broom handle. You can also take its internal temperature to check that the bacteria are doing their job. Turn the compost pile when its internal temperature is between 130 and 140 degrees Fahrenheit.

There are differing opinions on composting food prepared with oils, such as bread or baked goods or dressed salads. Also some say weeds are compostable but many others say you can't count on your compost to be hot enough to kill off weed seeds, which you do not want to add to your plantings, for sure. Herbivore animal manure, such as chicken, cow or horse manure, works well if you have access to it. We feel our vegetables are even developing their own terroir, the unique taste of a certain location and growing conditions, because of the closed system our goats and chickens contribute to, that nourishes the farm's soil which in turn feeds them.

If you do not have access to much "brown," think about relieving a suburbanite of some leaves, a stable of some hay or animal bedding, or a shop of their cardboard or crumbled brown bags. Starbucks or any coffee shop has tons of coffee grounds to contribute to your "green" proportion and the coffee filters will compost well too.

Be sure to use your rich soil in next year's garden. The payoff in your vegetables will be worth the effort! ❖

Well before you scoop out the rich soil, you're ahead of the game if you compost. The first benefit is the lesson it teaches on waste and on garbage. Yard and kitchen wastes make up about thirty percent of the waste stream in the US, so composting can play a big part in reducing waste overall. Even some forward-looking restaurants and municipalities are now connecting to farms to do just that.

WINTER

RESTORATION AND REFLECTION

What was I thinking when I went out without a hat and my high boots? Now, I can't crack the ice in the bucket with my foot. I'll have to run some water to loosen it but I think the warm water has almost run out. I can barely tip over this fourth bucket to dump it out. That natural ice bucket shape is only good for a great champagne and caviar fantasy. Well, not right now. Okay, what's next? The ATV is loaded with grain and the girls still have to be fed. Oh hell; it won't start.

The farm is so very quiet in the winter. I can almost hear the soil rebuilding under the snow and the new herd growing in the does' bellies. There's no sun at 6:30 a.m. when I let the dogs out. Icicles hang off the gutters, the birdhouses have white hats and miniature drifts gather on each fence grid. I see I'll have to shovel a pathway for the hens; those Chicken Littles think the sky is falling when it snows but my girls do fine with snow. My footsteps are muffled as I head for the goat barn alone in the quiet, grateful that there isn't freezing rain. A whispering breeze moves the surface of the packed snow where the only tracks now are made by the cat.

Because I'm a little late this morning, the does are not so polite and they bang at the door to get into the milking room where I feed them. I block their onslaught with my body and call the first group of does by name. They stick with their routine, entering by sixes, in the same group every time.

"Fiona, Ashanti, Carly, let's get going, get going, move it!" I shout. "I want you girls up on the stand." I don't really need to yell; they hop right up onto the milking stand to be fed a supplement of grain which

helps them to grow strong babies. The six-by-six feeding means no one gets more than her share or has to compete for feed in the pen. It also gives me a chance to pass my hands over them, making a quick check of their condition. This morning this group of does is fine. Their eyes are clear and their tail ends are clean. Ashanti and Carly had last year off from kidding so it's shocking to see how broad they are this year. I pat Fiona, who is also getting rounder and rounder. I'm hoping their births will be easy. Dione is supposedly pregnant—but is she? Note to self: try to breed her again? It's getting late in the season but she's a good milker that I'll want to have on the milk line next season.

If it were milking season now, I'd crank up the Barn Mix CD that Cara made for me (one song by each of the does' namesakes) and rock out to "R-E-S-P-E-C-T" as Aretha jumps onto the milking stand. But no soundtrack today to disrupt the calm and solitude. I'll just get the feeding done after I scold Carrie out of the way of the exit door. This little, horned doe is Shania's orphan, fostered by Dione; she was nursed for five months instead of bottle-fed so she's more skittish and avoids handling. I may have to nudge her along but if I'm not careful, I'll come home with souvenir crescent-shaped bruises on my legs from her horns.

My body is so attuned to the goats' rhythms that I still wake up early, but in the winter I can at least roll over for an hour or even luxuriate for two hours if Ron or Kevin can help with the farm chores. Of course, the team needs rest now too and the interns have moved on. The daily pressures and obligations relent and just running the farm feels like a vacation. This is the time for my hands and feet to heal, to rest, eat better and build the endurance and physical strength the next spring will require. I restore myself for the next round, find time to weave again and attend to my list.

In the winter, I can revel in the quiet pleasure of considering my own breakfast. I don't have goat milk to pour on it but should I have maple granola? The chickens are still giving enough eggs for a farm omelet. And toast with our own honey or apple butter? No more just grabbing the carbs on hand, no skipping the meal altogether like I do in the crazy-busy spring when I've already put in a six-hour workday by noon. Now I can do the chores on automatic pilot with head space to spare for noticing, daydreaming and planning.

And what's for dinner? Will it be my inter- pretation of that goat cheese and artichoke strata, my short cut of The Elms Restaurant's Chef Brendan Walsh's winter squash soup with apple (that Mark and I can live off for days), or my black bean chili? I can flavor one of my favorite hearty soups with the rind of that amazing three year-old Parmesan Ken Skovron shared with me and serve it with Dan Leader's great Bread Alone bread. I'm ready for the comfort memories, the cuddly food that our bodies seem to want in the winter; I've even resurrected my crockpot for chef Erica Wallace's beef burgundy.

Despite the cold and quiet, Rainbeau Ridge is growing all around me. The Comfort Food cooking class series that we run in the farmhouse kitchen sells out. Registration for all three children's programs, Roots,

Buds and Sprouts, is filled and Karen is keeping waiting lists already for the spring sessions. Customers are not trooping into the farmhouse but they follow the farm on the website and our GoatKeepers are all signed up and watching the progress of "their" goat's pregnancy on the BarnCam. When the kids start dropping in March, the children will be there to watch. Next season's volunteers are signing up to garden or to take care of the new kids.

Even in this period of relative calm, my Post-its spread and my bulletin board lists keep getting longer.

A January List:
　　Feb. panel: what to say?
　　CAP—review writeups
　　Red Cross first aid class
　　Quilting for kids: library books, mockup, plan for
　　　　Sprouts
　　Staff meetings: establish goals: marketing, how to hold
　　　　expenses, get greener, organizational chart.

In what passes for down time, I have farm personnel to hire, interns to pick, financials to run and new accounts to establish. Sometimes the mindless TV I watch while I exercise in the morning can distract me, but usually a notebook is close at hand. I'm scrawling: spring vaccinations for the does, update website, applications for the farmers markets. As I am retrenching, I'm also sticking up those Post-its until I drop into an occasional brain-dead winter evening in front of the fire.

Maybe I'll find time for the pile of books I've been accumulating next to my bed. In it are several novels friends have recommended, recent non-fiction, especially about environmental history, and daydream guidebooks for South Africa and Patagonia. I may even have an hour to cull and organize all those family photos or to visit the horses with a carrot. Later today, I resolve to call my patient, long-neglected, understanding friends, those precious ones with whom I can pick up as if nothing has gotten between us since my life on the farm began.

Sometimes in this season, I can even manage to get off the farm to visit my family in warm Florida or tour other cheesemakers' farms. I usually make any trip a busman's holiday too by checking out local cheese shops and stalking cheesemongers. Even when I volunteered in

South Africa, we were in the garden. The women and children laughed as I tried out my five Zulu words for soil, sun, water, leaf and grow. And part of the fun of leaving is coming back to see how much more pregnant the does are. It's staggering that in less than eight weeks, the dramatic season of life and of death will start again.

A REAL FARMER

Sitting in front of the fireplace, I reflect on this past spring's kidding. Missy seemed to be laboring as she should have at 10:45 p.m. and I could see she would be at it awhile longer. But when I checked a couple of hours later, her labor was not progressing. Reaching inside her, I felt the malpresentation: the kid was already out of its sac and its head was turned away from the birth canal. To survive, it had to be delivered right away. As I tried to turn the kid inside her, Missy screamed in pain so pitifully that Kelly heard her cries from the farmhouse and rushed to help me. In the dark of a cold spring night, we tried for over three hours to save Missy and the fifteen-pound kid, but to no avail. Finally, I understood that Missy would not live despite our best efforts and that nothing more could be done. At the break of dawn, Kelly and I urgently needed a change of scene. My wrists and forearms were swollen and ringed with purple bruises from the struggle but my emotional exhaustion was greater than the physical pains. After hot showers and a change of clothes, we shared breakfast at the local diner. In the booth, we sat in silence. When we returned to the farm and the work left undone, we exchanged a brief and reassuring hug and resumed our chores. Life goes on.

In this inward-turning season, I have time to contemplate the dilemmas and lessons like this that the other seasons have presented. The dormant landscape, almost-hibernating animals and sleeping environment invite reflection, bringing back memories of past kidding seasons on the farm. I know first hand that death is part of life and out of respect for life, my responsibility goes beyond the goats' economic value. I know that I will always make an effort to save every goat in trouble

and will treat every single one well in the short time each has under my care. With each year, I have more confidence, greater competence and fewer apologies to make. Now, I reframe my own question: not, "Am I a real farmer?" but, "How do I balance being the compassionate farmer and the practical farmer? How do I reconcile those two sets of values?"

Without hesitation, I give my all to save even a weak buckling I cannot keep, like Natalie's singleton, a runt that came in a not-so-easy delivery. Every year a few kids must be coddled or boosted a little to stand and nurse well, but if left to nature to take its course, this kid would have died. The buckling wasn't standing and couldn't nurse. I put him in a large dog cage in my kitchen and tubed him, which entailed feeding him milk through a length of soft rubber hose down his esophagus into his belly while avoiding his lungs. This more assertive intervention meant feeding him one ounce at a time around the clock. I chose to tube him even knowing he would be sold off the farm and thankfully, he survived, also saving his mother Natalie. Returning him to her for even his last few days on the farm lifted her depression and her health improved.

Should this compassionate farmer go to the same lengths for a doeling born with a bad leg? The practical farmer would not order x-rays and treatment for a three-week old kid. Still, my scrappy doe, Norah, broke her leg at three weeks old. "What would a farmer do?" I had asked vet Dan, who would become my lifeline in this business. "Shoot the goat," I guessed he was thinking, but instead he gave me a different choice. "Pin and plate her for fifteen-hundred dollars." She had cost me thirty. Was I a wimp or a hardass? Was there no alternative? Vet Dan relented, "Splint her leg and in the worst case, she'll be gimpy." That sounded fine to me. I kept her in a dog cage in a utility room across from my kitchen door for a few weeks until she healed. As it turned out, she was not gimpy and grew into a healthy milker and a great mother. She went on to kid uneventfully four times.

Even as I evolve as a "real farmer," or grow as a "different farmer," who cries more briefly, I still feel the pain and loss of the goats I know so well. As I negotiate the balance between compassion and practicality, I hope I never lose my love and appreciation for them and the caring commitment in the face of loss, the soul of what moves me to farm each day.

In order to produce milk for my cheese, the does must give birth. Because I breed them out of necessity, I know the births will yield males I cannot use on a dairy farm and eventually more females than I can handle, even if I plan to increase my herd. The first couple of years, I placed the neutered males as pets and sold any surplus females as future milkers. But as the herd grew, I understood that beyond the dairy business, I was in the meat business whether I liked it or not. The bucks had to be moved off the farm and inevitably would be raised to be eaten. I am a carnivore myself but the experience of confronting the goats as a food source is something I wish I didn't have to do. Nevertheless, I have committed to treating all of them well, no matter what the outcome. I also ensure that those I sell are raised in good conditions by the best possible hands, then slaughtered humanely and not wasted.

In winter, the physical R and R is essential to me and the time for contemplation is all too brief. I do allow myself one moment of self-congratulatory satisfaction about the year that's passed. We got a lot done: our herd and cheese production doubled; Sprouts' classes doubled too; In Lisa's Kitchen went year-round; the garden was ever more beautiful and productive; and the farm's public presence and reputation continue to grow. Now before I know it, I'll have to stick a bookmark in my novel and push to weave one more scarf off the loom. Soon, we'll be shearing again so I'll have to add last year's wool that I never spun to this year's pile. The seed catalogues are arriving and those routine spring vaccinations, which are given four weeks before birthing, signal that the period of restoration is about to end. Here it all comes again. 🙢

The winter kitchen gives me the cozy, warm dishes and the recuperation
I need in this season. In the recipes I have assembled here, you'll see the
same love of nurturing hat brought me to farming.

CHEESE PUFFS

These bite size puffs are terrific hors d'oeuvres. For variety, they can be stuffed and are great accompaniments for a soup or salad.

INGREDIENTS

8 Tbsp butter

1 cup water

$1/2$ cups flour

4 eggs

4 ounces fresh goat cheese

DIRECTIONS

Preheat oven to 350 degrees.

Line cookie sheet with Silpat or parchment paper.

In small saucepan, mix water and butter and heat over low until butter is melted.

Remove from heat.

Stir in flour with wooden spoon.

One at a time, add eggs and combine thoroughly. (Batter will look glossy.)

Keep stirring until it begins to dull.

Quickly beat in goat cheese.

Fill piping bag fitted with large tip with batter and pipe into small nugget size pieces onto lined cookie sheet.

Place pan in oven and bake for 15 minutes or until golden brown.

Remove from oven and cool on rack.

Yields 3 dozen puffs

Options:

Add finely minced herbs, such as 1 tsp chives, to the batter.

Can serve as is or cut open top and stuff with pureed broccoli. Return cut top and plate attractively.

Alternatively, pipe all batter into ring shape, approximately 8" in diameterand bake about 20 minutes or until golden brown.

CORIANDER & ROSEMARY
GOAT CHEESE LOG

As a log to be served on crackers, sliced into a salad or made into little bite-sized nuggets, this is a winning combination. Try setting the slices on top of a burger or steak too!

INGREDIENTS

1 Tbsp butter

1 cup pecans

$\frac{1}{2}$ tsp salt

2 ChevreLait, room temperature

1 tsp fresh rosemary, minced

1 tsp ground coriander

DIRECTIONS

Preheat oven to 350 degrees.

Melt butter and toss pecans in it along with sugar and salt.

Place mixture on jelly roll pan or cookie sheet lined with a Silpat or parchment paper.

Bake about 10 minutes or until toasted.

Let cool and chop pecans by hand or in a food processor until finely chopped.

Cream goat cheese with rosemary and coriander. (Mixture may need to be chilled in order to handle.)

Roll cheese into log form and coat with pecans.

Wrap in plastic wrap and chill until serving. May be made one day ahead.

Yields 16 slices or 32 nuggets

Serving Suggestions:

Slice log and top your favorite salad.

Alternative:

Roll mixture into grape size balls (instead of log) and stack like savory truffles and serve as hors d'oeuvres.

Take small size balls and flatten slightly. Heat fry pan with a tiny bit of olive oil and lightly warm goat cheese before adding warmed discs to salad.

SAVORY PALMIERS

These beautiful pastries make elegant hors d'oeuvres, but make extra to have as scrumptious leftovers.

INGREDIENTS

One sheet puff pastry dough, defrosted

6 ounces sun-dried tomatoes, drained of oil and finely chopped

1 clove garlic, minced

3 ounces pine nuts, toasted and coarsely chopped

3 Tbsp firm ChevreLog, grated

DIRECTIONS

Preheat oven to 400 degrees.

Combine tomatoes, garlic, pine nuts and cheese into a paste.

Roll out 2 puff pastry sheets, each to an 8"x 14" rectangle.

Spread each with half of tomato mixture to within $1/4$" of edges of each sheet.

Working on the long side of each pastry sheet, roll up one side at a time into the center of the pastry sheet.

The rolls should meet in the middle.

Refrigerate at least 20 minutes.

Removing from the refrigerator, slice roll into $1/2$" pieces and place flat on cookie sheet lined with parchment paper or a silpat, with generous space between each.

Bake until crisp, about 15 minutes.

Yields 32 pieces

Note: This flavor profile easily lends itself to the addition of a savory herb, such as sage, oregano, thyme or basil.

BEGGAR'S PURSES IN WILD MUSHROOM SOUP

These simple accompaniments make any soup more elegant or create instantly impressive hors d'oeuvres—they taste terrific too!

BEGGAR'S PURSES

INGREDIENTS

Three sheets phyllo dough (defrosted per package directions)
$1/4$ cup unsalted butter, melted
6 ounce fresh goat cheese, softened

DIRECTIONS

Preheat oven to 350 degrees.

Lay one phyllos sheet dough on a clean surface (use a cutting surface).

Brush with melted butter.

Repeat this two more times with phyllo sheets and butter.

Cut dough into twelve 3- x 4-inch squares (using a pizza cutter can ensure success).

Place a spoonful of goat cheese in the center of each phyllo square.

Pull up corners of phyllo dough, pinching it just above the goat cheese and gathering edges just below the top to make the beggar's purse.

It can be placed on a baking sheet lined with parchment paper or placed gently in a mini-muffin tin to help the purse keep its shape.

At this point, purses can be placed in the refrigerator until ready for baking and use.

Place baking tray in oven for 10-15 minutes or until golden brown.

Remove and serve warm.

Yields 8 pieces

SOUP

INGREDIENTS

2 Tbsp butter

$1/3$ cup shallots, minced

6 ounces each of fresh shitake, oyster, crimini mushrooms

2 ounces dried porcini mushrooms, soaked in warm water to cover

8 cups stock

DIRECTIONS

Melt butter in large pot over medium-high heat.

Add shallots and sauté until just golden, about 5 minutes.

Add all fresh mushrooms and sauté until they begin to soften, about 8 minutes.

Drain porcini of liquid and reserve water

Add porcini to mushroom mixture and continue to cook over low flame for 2-3 minutes.

Strain reserved porcini mushroom liquid through fine strainer or use paper towel or cheese cloth.

Add this liquid and the stock to the pot and slowly stir in broth.

Bring soup to boil.

Reduce heat and simmer uncovered 10 minutes.

Take $1/3$ to -of the mushrooms and puree in food processor.

Return to pot and stir thoroughly.

Process more to your desired texture for the soup.

Season with salt & pepper to taste.

Ladle into bowls and top with Beggar's Purses.

Yields 8 servings

Simple Additions:

Add chopped, toasted pecans inside of the purse on top of the cheese.

Add herbs to the cheese before assembling the purse.

CURRIED APPLE & BUTTERCUP SQUASH SOUP WITH PISTACHIO-COATED CROTTINS

Brendan Walsh, Chef, Brendan's at The Elms, Ridgefield, CT

SOUP

INGREDIENTS

3 pounds buttercup squash (can use butternut squash)

1/2 pound onions

1/4 pound celery, sliced into 1/2 inch pieces

1/4 pound carrots, sliced into 1/2 inch chunks

2 ounces butter or oil

2 garlic cloves, peeled

2 Macoun apples, peeled and cut into 1/2 inch cubes

1 1/2 oz brandy

1 1/2 oz lemon juice

3/4 tsp cinnamon

Pinch* crushed red pepper

Pinch* grated nutmeg

Pinch* ground cloves

Pinch* ground allspice

1 bay leaf

1 Tbsp light brown sugar

1/8 cup yellow curry powder

1/2 gallon water, vegetable stock or chicken stock

Salt & pepper to taste

*Pinch is just under 1/8 teaspoon.

DIRECTIONS

Preheat oven to 350 degrees.

Line baking sheet with foil, coating with non-stick spray or silpat.

Cut the squash in half, remove seeds and place skin side up on baking sheet and roast for 30-40 minutes until flesh is tender.

Remove from oven, and scrape away from skin, tossing out the skin.

Puree the squash in food processor and set aside.

While squash is baking, in large pot, melt butter or heat oil over low heat and add onions, celery and carrots.

Sweat the vegetables, ensuring that they do not brown, about 8 minutes.

Add the garlic and continue to cook until mixture is softened.

Add the water or stock.

Add the seasonings, sugar, lemon juice, brandy and apples.

Bring to boil for five minutes.

Reduce heat to low and then add the squash puree.

Continue cooking for 35 minutes.

Puree in food processor.

Bring back to desired heat before serving.

Serve with pistachio-coated goat cheese crottin.

PISTACHIO-COATED GOAT CHEESE CROTTINS

INGREDIENTS

8 ounces Rainbeau Ridge ChevreLait, room temperature

$1/4$ cup flour

1 egg, beaten with 1 Tbsp water

$1/2$ cup pistachio nuts, finely chopped

Canola oil for cooking

DIRECTIONS

To make discs, roll the goat cheese to form log about 4 inches long.

Refrigerate about 30 minutes or until sliceable.

Cut goat cheese log into eight $1/2$" slices and dust lightly on all surfaces
with flour.

Dip floured slices into beaten eggs and dredge in chopped pistachios.

Refrigerate until ready for use.

In sauté pan, heat a small amount of oil over medium heat and gently warm
the pistachio-coated goat cheese discs, turning to warm throughout.

Yields 8 generous servings

FARRO, SQUASH, APPLE & GOAT CHEESE SALAD

Nicki Sizemore, Chef/Food Writer, Fairfield, CT

INGREDIENTS

¹/₂ cups farro

1 2-pound butternut squash, peeled and cut into ¹/₂-inch dice (4 cups diced)

6 cloves garlic, unpeeled

2 tsp minced fresh sage, divided

1¹/₂ tsp balsamic vinegar

1¹/₂ Tbsp plus ¹/₄ cup extra virgin olive oil, divided

Salt & freshly ground black pepper

³/₄ cup pecans

1¹/₂ Tbsp maple syrup

2 Tbsp apple cider vinegar

1 crisp apple (such as Fuji, Jonagold or Gala), cored

2-4-ounces Rainbeau Ridge fresh goat cheese, crumbled

Fried sage leaves (optional)

DIRECTIONS

In a large bowl, cover the farro with cold water and soak for 25 minutes.

Preheat the oven to 400 degrees.

In a large bowl, toss the diced butternut squash, garlic cloves, 1 ¹/₂ teaspoons sage, balsamic vinegar, 1¹/₂ tablespoons olive oil and a generous pinch of salt and pepper.

Pour coated squash onto large baking sheet.

Roast 25-30 minutes, turning occasionally, until the squash is tender and caramelized around the edges.

Taste and season with additional salt and pepper if needed, setting aside when done.

While the squash bakes, make the maple pecans and the farro.

In small bowl, toss pecans with 1 Tbsp maple syrup and a pinch of salt.

Pour pecans onto a small baking sheet, lined with aluminum foil.

Bake 5 minutes, or until the nuts are a shade darker in color and aromatic.

Transfer immediately to a plate to cool, then coarsely chop.

Drain the farro and place in a medium pot.

Cover with 2 inches of water and bring to a boil (covered).

Reduce the heat and simmer, uncovered, 15-20 minutes, or until tender.

Drain and transfer to a large bowl.

Add the roasted squash, reserving the garlic cloves for the dressing.

To make the dressing, squeeze the garlic out if its skins into a small bowl and mash it into a paste with a pinch of salt.

Mix with the apple cider vinegar, $1/2$ Tbsp maple syrup, the remaining $1/2$ teaspoon sage, and a pinch of salt and pepper.

Whisk in the remaining $1/4$ cup extra virgin olive oil.

Yield 6 servings

Assembly:

Right before serving, cut the apple into a $1/2$-inch dice and add to the farro, along with the chopped pecans.

Toss the salad with the dressing.

Add salt & pepper if needed.

Top with the goat cheese.

Top with fried sage leaves, if using.

ARTICHOKE STRATA

Enormously satisfying, this easy to make recipe is perfect for brunch, takes advantage of leftover bread and can be assembled ahead of time.

INGREDIENTS

2 cups milk

$1/4$ cup olive oil from artichoke hearts (see below)

1 pound sourdough bread (cut into 1" cubes)

5 eggs

1 Tbsp garlic, chopped

1 $1/2$ tsp salt

$1/2$ tsp pepper

$1/2$ tsp nutmeg

2 Tbsp sage, chopped

1 Tbsp thyme or parsley, chopped

1 tsp oregano

3 jars (6 $1/2$ ounces) marinated artichoke hearts (drained – use reserved oil in above)

1 cup Fontina cheese grated

1 cup Parmesan cheese grated

8 ounces fresh goat cheese

DIRECTIONS

Preheat oven to 350 degrees.

Prepare 13"x9" baking dish with butter or non-stick spray.

In large bowl, soak bread in oil and milk, let bread absorb all liquid.

In separate bowl, whisk eggs and seasonings together.

Add egg mixture to soaked bread.

Mix in remaining ingredients.

Pour into prepared baking dish.

Bake for 45 minutes to 1 hour until top is golden brown.

Yields 10-12 servings

LASAGNA ROLLUPS

Layering lasagna noodles is expected … so why not try these individual portions, rolled for a great presentation?

INGREDIENTS

8 whole wheat lasagna noodles

24 ounces tomato sauce

16 ounces fresh goat cheese

2 cups spinach, cooked and drained, or other vegetables

1 cup mushrooms

Parmesan cheese, grated

DIRECTIONS

Preheat oven to 350 degrees.

In 9"x13" glass baking dish, spread tomato sauce lightly on the bottom.

In large pot, boil water, salting lightly and cook lasagna noodles until al dente.

Drain and rinse noodles quickly in warm water.

Lay each noodle flat and spread evenly with fresh goat cheese, ending 1 inch from end.

Add spinach, mushrooms and any other vegetables—the key is spreading the ingredients evenly and flat.

Roll each noodle carefully toward end with 1 inch margin.

Place in baking dish with end down.

When all noodles are rolled, top each with a spoonful of tomato sauce.

Sprinkle with Parmesan cheese, to taste.

Bake for 20-25 minutes.

Serve warm.

Yields 8 servings

LAMB & EGGPLANT PANINI

Daniel Leader, Owner/Author, Bread Alone Bakery, Boiceville, NY

INGREDIENTS

2 all-purpose flatbreads or pita breads

1 Tbsp olive oil

1/3 cup Baba Ghanoush (recipe follows)

8 thin slices of leg of lamb

2 ounces Rainbeau Ridge fresh goat cheese

1 Tbsp finely chopped parsley

DIRECTIONS

Heat the panini or sandwich press according to manufacturer's instructions.

If using pita breads, slice in half with serrated knife.

Brush both sides of the breads with the olive oi.l

Spread baba ghanoush on one side of each flatbread or the bottom halves of the pita breads.

Arrange sliced lamb on top of the baba ghanoush.

Sprinkle the goat cheese over the lamb.

Sprinkle parsley on top of the cheese.

Fold over the flatbreads to cover the filling, or top with the top halves of the pita breads.

Put the 'sandwiches' on the press, pull the top down and cook until they are browned and crisp, 4 to 7 minutes, depending upon how hot your machine is.

Carefully remove from the press and serve immediately.

Yields 2 sandwiches

BABA GHANOUSH

INGREDIENTS

1 cup eggplant slices, packed in olive oil, rinsed and drained, and patted
   dry

1 Tbsp tahini (sesame spread)

1 tsp fresh lemon juice

1 small garlic clove, finely chopped

salt & freshly ground pepper

DIRECTIONS

Combine eggplant, tahini, lemon juice and garlic in food processor and
   process until smooth.

Scrape into a bowl, if using right away, or a small airtight container if
   storing.

Season with salt and pepper

This will keep, tightly covered, in the refrigerator up to 3 days

Yields 1 cup

Rainbeau Ridge Note—using fresh eggplant in season:

There's no doubt that eggplant slices save time, but in season, we roast
eggplant daily—so I have some on hand to make the Baba Ghanoush from
fresh eggplant. I like to use small and firm eggplant, cut in half lengthwise.
Brushed with a little olive oil, Roast at 350 degrees, skin side down, until
almost tender (watch carefully as the time varies by size of eggplant). Turn
over and finish until tender. Scoop out and use in recipes. Larger eggplant
may be bitter, so slice into $1/2$" thick disks, salt both sides and set in colander
to drain before roasting.

MAC 'N CHEESE

Enjoy this elegant comfort food with a glass of white wine by the fire on a winter's day.

INGREDIENTS

8 ounces macaroni

2 Tbsp butter

2 Tbsp flour

2 cups milk (any type)

4 ounces fresh goat cheese

4 ounces firm ChevreLog, grated

4 Tbsp dried bread crumbs

1 Tbsp fresh sage or thyme, minced finely

4 ounces fresh goat cheese for topping

Salt & pepper to taste

DIRECTIONS

Preheat oven to 350 degrees.

Prepare a 9" square baking pan with non-stick spray.

Cook macaroni in lightly salted boiling water about 10 minutes until barely tender, then drain and set aside.

In a saucepan, melt butter over low heat.

Stir in the flour thoroughly to create a paste and continue to cook for 1 minute.

Slowly add milk, whisking constantly to create a creamy sauce, then cook an additional 5 minutes before removing from heat.

Add first two goat cheeses, whisking to make the sauce smooth.

Combine macaroni and cheese sauce in a bowl and pour into prepared baking pan.

In small bowl, mix bread crumbs and herbs and sprinkle over macaroni.

Add salt and pepper to taste.

Distribute the remaining goat cheese evenly over the top.

Bake in oven for about 20-25 minutes until heated through and cheese is bubbly.

Yields 6-8 servings

Note: Truffle salt is a real treat and significantly enhances this fabulous dish.

STUFFED FRENCH TOAST

Buying brioche? Buy two—one for now and one for this wonderful breakfast treat in the morning.

INGREDIENTS

1 loaf day old brioche or challah

12 ounces fresh goat cheese

$1/4$ cup honey

1 tsp vanilla

$1/2$ cup medium chopped walnuts, almonds or pecans, optional

4 eggs

$1/2$ cup milk

$1/2$ tsp vanilla

Butter for frying

> *Garnish options:* Confectioners sugar, home-made maple syrup, banana slices, preserves and berries (from frozen in season)

DIRECTIONS

Slice bread into 1" thick pieces.

Cream goat cheese with honey and vanilla.

If desired, combine nuts into cheese mixture.

Spread mixture liberally on one piece of bread and press a second slice on top to form a sandwich.

In medium bowl, whisk eggs thoroughly and add in milk and vanilla.

Dip bread sandwich into egg mixture and put into well-buttered frying pan or griddle pan.

Cook over medium heat about 3 minutes each side or until golden in color.

Slice on the diagonal and overlap as you place the French toast on the center of the plate and dust with confectioners sugar.

Drizzle with syrup and place berries or preserves along side.

Yields 4-6 servings

QUINOA & WILD RICE PILAF WITH POMEGRANATE SEEDS

Taste, texture and colorful ingredients define this healthy and delicious dish.

INGREDIENTS

2 tsp olive oil

1 medium onion minced

1 cup wild rice, rinsed and drained

$1/2$ cup quinoa

3 cups chicken or vegetable stock

1 cup pomegranate juice*

$1/3$ cup walnuts, toasted

1 cup pomegranate seeds*

2 tsp lemon zest

1 bunch scallions minced

6 ounces fresh goat cheese, room temperature

DIRECTIONS

Heat oil in a large saucepan over medium heat.

Add onion and cook until softened.

Add wild rice and quinoa and stir until evenly coated.

Add chicken or vegetable stock and bring to a boil.

Reduce heat to low, cover and simmer until both grains are tender, about 30 to 45 minutes.

In small saucepan, bring pomegranate juice to a boil.

Continue to cook over medium flame until liquid is reduced to $1/2$ cup.

Toast walnuts in a small, dry skillet over medium-low heat, stirring constantly, 2 to 3 minutes.

Transfer to a dish to cool. To cooked grains, add pomegranate seeds, lemon zest, scallions and toasted walnuts.

Pour on pomegranate reduction and toss thoroughly.

Stir in goat cheese.

Serve warm.

* How do you get the beautiful seeds out of a pomegranate and how do you make juice?

Prepare a bowl of ice cold water, large enough to fit a pomegranate. Next, cut off the 'crown' at the top and carefully cut out the flesh at the top until you reach the seeds. Next, make at least four vertical slices into the pomegranate (without cutting all the way into the center). Now you can get to the seeds. Insert your thumbs in the top and break the pomegranate into sections. Place the pomegranate pieces into the bowl of ice water (you can wait 5 minutes to make this easier) and coax out the seeds. The seeds should fall to the bottom and you can compost the seed pockets. Gently drain the seeds and pat them dry before using. One pomegranate should yield about one cup of seeds (and the largest pomegranates don't necessarily have lots more seeds).

To make juice, grind the pomegranate seeds in a small grinder or blender and strain to remove the ground seeds. Alternatively, you can purchase unsweetened pomegranate juice and seeds in the market.

Yields 6 servings

207

GARLIC SMASHED POTATOES

Smashed potatoes, unlike their more refined cousin, mashed potatoes, are more rustic and call for skins on. While Russets are favorites for mashed versions, I like to use new potatoes or Yukon golds since the skins are more appealing to eat.

INGREDIENTS

3 pounds red new potatoes or Yukon Gold potatoes, skin on

1 tsp salt

$1/2$ cup whole milk

4-6 ounces fresh goat cheese, softened

2-3 garlic cloves, minced

salt & pepper

DIRECTIONS

Wash potatoes thoroughly.

If large, cut in even sized pieces to ensure more uniform cooking.

Generously cover potatoes with cold water and bring to boil.

Reduce flame to simmer and cook until tender; about 15-20 minutes.

Drain potatoes and transfer to work bowl.

Using a large fork or utility spoon, smash potatoes coarsely.

Add milk until combined.

Add garlic and goat cheese.

Salt & pepper to taste.

Yield 4-6 servings

Note: For a spring version, use chives and be sure to use the chive blossoms for the delicate lavender color; peas are excellent additions too.

CHOCOLATE TRUFFLES

Ok, I have to admit that I don't tell anyone the main ingredient in these before having them enjoy these treats. After all, it isn't your obvious pairing. But the influence of cinnamon and chocolate on the goat cheese is a winner!

INGREDIENTS

6 ounces fresh goat cheese

6 ounces semi-sweetened chocolate, broken into small pieces or morsels

2 Tbsp confectioners sugar

$1/_2$ tsp vanilla

$1/_2$ tsp cinnamon

$1/_4$ cup Dutch cocoa powder

DIRECTIONS

Melt chocolate in a double boiler or carefully in the microwave.

Stir until smooth and set aside to cool slightly.

In mixer, beat cheese, sugar, vanilla and cinnamon until light and fluffy.

Mix in cooled chocolate until well blended.

Chill in the refrigerator for 45 minutes. (if the base gets too cold, it's hard to shape into balls)

Remove from refrigerator and, using a small scoop, form 1" balls and coat with cocoa.

Put truffles on a cookie sheet lined with waxed or parchment paper.

Chill about 30 minutes.

Yields 12-18 truffles

Substitutions:

A great alternative to the cinnamon is $1/_8$ tsp almond extract.

Finely ground nuts are a delicious coating in lieu of the cocoa powder.

209

LEMON ORANGE DESSERT FRITTERS

Curl up with these and some hot cocoa or warm apple cider by the fire on a winter afternoon.

INGREDIENTS

16 ounces fresh goat cheese

zest of 1 lemon

zest of 1 orange

4 Tbsp sugar

1 tsp baking powder

2 eggs

8 Tbsp flour

2 cups canola oil for frying

juice of 1 lemon

juice of 1 orange

4 Tbsp honey

Powdered sugar for finishing

DIRECTIONS

Preheat oven to 300 degrees.

In a mixing bowl, stir together goat cheese, zests, sugar, baking powder and eggs until well blended and refrigerate 15 minutes.

In fry pan, heat oil to 375 degrees.

With small scoop or tablespoon, scoop batter and roll into ball, coating outside with flour.

Gently drop ball in oil off of a tablespoon and fry a few at a time until deep golden brown and crisp (the fritters will flatten out, don't crowd them).

Remove to plate or rack and drain on paper towels.

Keep warm in 300 degree oven as you complete the fritters.

In small saucepan, reduce lemon & orange juices to half over medium low heat.

Stir in honey and remove from heat.

Drizzle finished fritters with citrus-honey reduction, dust with powdered sugar and serve.

Yields 24 pieces

SWEET SPOTS

These cheese-filled chocolate cupcakes are not for kids only!

INGREDIENTS

8 ounces fresh goat cheese

1 egg

$1/_2$ cup confectioners sugar

$1/_2$ tsp vanilla

1 $1/_2$ cups all-purpose flour

1 cup granulated sugar

$1/_3$ cup unsweetened cocoa powder, sifted

1 tsp baking soda

$1/_2$ tsp salt

1 cup water

$1/_3$ cup vegetable oil

1 tsp vanilla

DIRECTIONS

Preheat oven to 350 degrees.

Line muffin tins with paper cups or lightly spray with non-stick cooking spray.

In a medium bowl, beat the goat cheese, egg, confectioners sugar,
$1/_2$ tsp vanilla until light and fluffy.

In a separate large bowl, mix together the flour, granulated sugar, cocoa,
baking soda and salt.

Make a well in the center and add the water, oil and 1 tsp vanilla.

Blend together until well blended.

Fill muffin cups halfway with the batter.

Add a dollop of the creamed cheese mixture.

Top off with remaining batter.

Bake in oven for 20 minutes or until toothpick comes out clean.

Let cool on rack before serving.

Yields 12 pieces

FINDING A CSA

SOMETIMES, DAYDREAMING OVER those lush seed catalogues in the depth of winter, do you wish for your very own farmer? Through Community Supported Agriculture (CSA), you can have one. CSA members purchase a share of a farmer's crop in advance and receive a bagful of vegetables every week during the growing season. This creates a win-win arrangement for a small farm and for consumers. The farmer receives capital upfront as he prepares for the planting season and is assured of a market for his produce. He can also provide a strong market to other producers. He builds loyalty and raises his profile in the community, contacting a ready-made support group, often pre-disposed to other sustainable efforts as well. The consumers have a grower, accountable to them, and so can proudly trust in the quality of what they receive.

The farmer, of course, is interested in growing what people will buy and eat. Smaller carrots? More Asian greens? Yellow tomatoes? Farmers thrive on hearing that a child who wouldn't touch beans and lettuce before now loves them. Interaction and feedback are available easily. And it's fun. You chat with your farmer and your fellow members. Your kids might be able to pick the peas they'll eat, pet goats or at least shake hands with the person who grew their food. You feel the gratitude and excitement at the source of your food.

Nationally, CSA farms have varied arrangements with the communities they serve. Some require actual work at the farm, manning pickup times, weeding or bookkeeping. Some organize boxfuls of produce weekly and deliver to a central site. Others require a trip to the

farm and a little time putting together your share. "Take 2 leeks," a sign above the table might say, or "Take one large and one small tomato." Some include only vegetables and others sell fruit, eggs, even flowers shares too, as well as access to other artisanal products, such as cheese, bread or local meat. Some allow choice, while others give members whatever is growing well that week.

As a CSA member, not only are you guaranteed to know where your food comes from, but in the exchange you will also discover other sources. Somebody will tell you about a u-pick raspberry farm that just opened or about a woman who makes the best pies from local fruit. You'll see and experiment with vegetables you have never eaten or cooked before, such as tomatillos, Jerusalem artichokes or ciogga beets. Too much totsoi? When you cook and freeze the produce, you'll be carrying your share beyond the season.

I became aware of CSA farms during our family's four-year stay in Japan, where community farm initiatives got under way in the early 1970s as a result of concerns about pesticide use and farmers' economic fragility. The American movement is credited to the European biodynamic agricultural tradition, based on the ideas of Austrian philosopher-educator Rudolf Steiner (1861-1925). Influenced by these two parallel strands, CSAs began in the US, simultaneously but independently, in 1986 at Indian Line Farm in South Egremont, Massachusetts and the Temple-Wilton Farm in Wilton, New Hampshire, two New England farms that are still thriving today.

Use winter time to locate a CSA in you area. The websites of a variety of local and national organizations can provide you with a list of accessible CSA farms. Contact the farms for the details of produce, price, pickup and whether any work is required. If the closest farm is still too far away, consider getting a group together that makes the farmer's delivery trip worthwhile. Or perhaps the farmer already comes to an area farmers market and you can pick up there. It's really like Christmas every week, whether you open up or stuff that bag with the freshest vegetables or choose your own from what's picked at its moment of perfection.

Our arrangement at Rainbeau Ridge is a modification we call a Community Agricultural Partnership, or CAP. To me, the term uses three words that communicate our level of quality and our values. I wanted to stress that we are in this together, the farm and the community, in a partnership of trust and economics. Customers already familiar with CSAs understand CAP because the term is close enough. To those who've never heard of such an arrangement, the acronym produces an opportunity to explain and a moment in which we can differentiate and market the farm.

The CAP is a more individualized arrangement. I knew my discerning market and wanted to create an upscale crop mix that was visually stunning and unusual. I wanted to build my credibility and our name by providing vegetables worth going out of your way for. Our members (a hundred in 2008 with a waiting list) have an account set up with an initial balance, which they buy down every week at the farm. They can also re-up their balance over the season. We offer produce, cheese, eggs and the products of several outside vendors, such as bread and beef and delicious baked goods that utilize many of our ingredients. ❖

THINK SEASONAL, EAT LOCAL

LET'S SAY YOU ALREADY are a regular at the closest farmers markets, you are a proud CSA member or vegetable gardener yourself, you've managed to find a connection for local eggs, cheese and pastured meats and poultry, and you buy fruit at area orchards whenever possible. You are simply glowing in the dark with health and virtue. Then, it frosts, the markets close up, the apples get mushy and boring, the last lamb has gone to slaughter and the cheesemaker is hunkered down until March.

Face the supermarket or health food store again? What to do to stay a locavore in the winter?

We are very far from purists at Rainbeau Ridge; we use citrus and olive oil with delight, thrive on exotic chocolate and almonds and default quickly to the grocery store for large-scale, event buying or a particular must-have ingredient for a favorite dish. Note the marinated artichoke hearts in our strata . . . yum! I've got my dark glasses on and my explanation handy for the afternoon I run into an acquaintance in the produce aisle who sees me buying pineapple or even a cake mix. Sometimes when I'm exhausted, I just need a slice of pizzeria pizza. It happens, it's life. Judgment and rigidity don't make busy lives easier or change people's habits. That's why we say, "One step at a time."

But local eating can go on past the warm weather and you will not be eating "nothing but potatoes" if you make the commitment. First, CSAs with winter shares and winter farmers markets are growing. The vendors at our closest farmers market made a deal with a local nursery to set up in one wing every Saturday all winter. Local bread, fruit, meats, prepared foods, and, yes, fresh vegetables are for sale and the nursery gets traffic it wouldn't otherwise. In January there was already cilantro, parsley, beets with their greens, kale and baby spinach. They are grown in unheated or minimally heated hoop houses or sometimes hydroponically (in water). While we do not continue our CAP all winter, at Rainbeau Ridge we use passive solar hoop houses to keep soil warm and extend our season. Bok choy and Swiss chard were growing happily in February.

Second, if properly stored, many vegetables will last well into our Northeast winter. Beets and winter squashes, sweet potatoes and cabbages, leeks, onions, shallots are all long-keeping and perfect for the comfort food cooking of winter around here. We can still loosen our definition mindfully, picking in-season citrus from Florida, for example, rather than plums from Chile, unendangered fish from New England and not from Argentina or the Mediterranean.

Admittedly, food miles and carbon footprint can be complicated to calculate and the conundrum of local vs. seasonal vs. humanely treated vs. pastured vs. organic can be hard to prioritize when it's all about getting dinner on the table. When the local lamb isn't available, do you choose pastured from New Zealand or conventionally-raised American from Colorado? Ask questions of your suppliers when you can; notice and question source labeling. Demand the products you'd like to see in your local store.

Helpful also is the third, easier-said-then-done solution of fore-thought; that is, the Ant's approach to planning ahead while the Grasshopper was fiddling. When the bounty is available, put it by. That doesn't have to mean canning or dehydrating, although neither is awfully difficult. In season, chop up and throw into a big pot whatever vegetables you've got; cook them gently, usually with no extra water needed, and freeze the result in quart bags. In the winter, defrost the bag just enough to slide the frozen vegetables into a soup pot, add broth to taste and a carbohydrate, if you like (cooked beans, rice, pasta, barley, etc.). Soup's on! These mixes make fast lasagna filling or pasta primavera too.

You can try bringing your herb plants into a sunny window before the frost; I've even had success growing lemons that way with care and maintenance. Otherwise, packets of mixed herb pesto can be frozen in ice cube trays and defrosted to slather on a roast chicken, add to a dip, sauce pasta, fold into cornbread or other quick breads or make a fresh-tasting salad dressing. Add the cheese when you defrost and use the pesto. Otherwise it dries out and looses flavor in the freezer. Our unmolded curds will freeze pretty well for cooking purposes, as will others, but expect the cheese to change texture somewhat in freezing.

I used to reprimand friends for eating berries in February but now if they see me sprinkling raspberries on a piece of pound cake for a winter dessert, I have a proud response: seasonal berries flash-freeze perfectly. Wash them gently, pat dry, spread them out on a cookie sheet or baking tin and freeze them for a few hours. After they have frozen, chip them off into freezer bags and you can simply pour them out in February, remembering the very hot sunny day you bought them from that nice farmer or picked them yourself from that bee-buzzing briar. Applesauce freezes well, as do lightly cooked and sweetened pears, plums or peaches.

The planning is worth it because the memories of those hot days are so thrilling and sustaining in the cold, dark months. So go ahead; put some California brown rice or Italian Reggiano Parmegiano into your minestrone. Squeeze a Meyer lemon onto your pears, poached with honey and stuffed with almond paste. Enjoy what the Global Village can bring us these days while at the same time you refocus your eating close to home with the rhythm of the year. ❖

Lay whole leaves or chiffonades of herbs between parchment paper or plastic wrap and roll them up to freeze. They won't defrost prettily, but can certainly be thrown directly into the stew pot. Herbs can also be chopped and mashed into soft butter, with garlic or without, to use later on baguettes or on top of a grass-fed steak.

MAKING MAPLE SYRUP

WHERE WOULD WINTER PANCAKES BE without maple syrup? As the Northeast emerges from winter, the sap rises like our hopes for spring. From mid-February to March, when nights are cool and days are warmer, we make maple syrup, one of the first locavore foods after the winter. The syrup tastes of four seasons on the farm, of the red leaves of autumn and the entire quiet winter, breaking up and turning sweet in spring.

We make our own syrup with the Sprouts kids each year; they help us tap the trees and collect the sap. When it's boiled down, they eat homemade waffles with the syrup they've helped make. We notice differences in color and flavor from tree to tree. My current favorite use of our sweet-smelling, gold-brown syrup is maple cream, made by mixing our tart, fresh cheese (or curd we've frozen) with our farm-collected syrup. The last of winter's root vegetables, such as winter squash, are exquisite when maple-glazed. Maple oatmeal and maple-walnut pie are pretty terrific too.

Even with very few sugar maples, you can make your own maple syrup, just like Native Americans did. Ask a neighbor if there isn't one in your yard and offer to share some syrup.

You'll need spiles, or spouts, sap containers, such as common gallon milk jugs, or quaint covered buckets, a few large collecting buckets and a sturdy large pot (or pan) to boil the sap in. You can try boiling it over wood on an outside hearth but you'll have to be lucky with the weather, keep stuff from falling into the pot and tend it carefully. If you boil it inside, make sure your kitchen venting fan is on or run a dehumidifier unless you have wallpaper to remove in the kitchen. Boiling sap produces a lot of moisture.

A sugar maple tree should be at least ten inches in diameter for one tap hole and bucket. For every additional eight inches in diameter, another tap hole and bucket may be added. For example, a tree twenty-six inches in diameter could be hung with three buckets. Drill a hole with a 7/16-inch drill bit about an inch and a half deep. Use a new site for the spout every year in unblemished bark at a convenient height. Drive the spout in so that it is tight and cannot be pulled out by hand, but don't overdrive it.

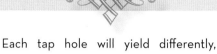

Each tap hole will yield differently, averaging between five to fifteen gallons of sap, but the ratio of sap to syrup is forty to one. Usually trees with lots of branches are better producers.

When the sap starts filling your collecting containers, pour it off into the larger buckets and keep it cool (outside in cool weather) until you're ready to cook it. You'll boil it slowly until it reaches 219 degrees Fahrenheit (the point at which it is sixty-six percent sugar, a measurement for which you'd need a special instrument). A candy thermometer will work for your small home production. The process will take hours (about four to five), so watch the pot very carefully to avoid burning the syrup. Don't let it evaporate to less than one-inch deep. You may need to move it a smaller pot as it boils down.

Filter the syrup through a purchased filter or a few folds of clean cheesecloth, or let it cool until the sediment drops to the bottom and ladle off the clean syrup carefully. You'll need to reheat the syrup to 180 degrees before pouring the hot syrup into clean, sterile canning jars and sealing them. Keep the jars in a cool place and once opened, refrigerate the syrup. Of course, I don't know how long the syrup will last anyway. Usually we use it right up. ❖

EPILOGUE

Martha alerts me that there were several calls for me so I pick up the pink message pad in the farmhouse. When I read down the list of messages, I just have to laugh at how complicated life has gotten. The local Audubon Society wants to discuss adopting our Sprouts curriculum. There's another from a new Connecticut cheese shop that has called to place an order, without even waiting for samples. A national magazine called too; they need to set up a photo shoot for their upcoming feature. Meanwhile a local kindergarten has incubated eggs and wonders if we can take the chicks off their hands. Add those to the e-mails I got this very morning with a request for a farm visit for next spring already and an invitation to speak at a farm-based education conference. The messages point out just how far I've come from a pair of goats. We've layered onto our local niche a developing regional presence and we're taking the first cautious steps into national visibility.

LIVING THE DREAM

The windows of the cheese house at this point in the farm's life cycle give me a perfect vantage point to view of all the components of Rainbeau Ridge's interdependent programs. From the east window, I can admire the bursting garden. Looking west, I can see the healthy does and the kids, intertwined and snoozing or turning in playful pirouettes. In the north, I see the goat barn in the distance and sometimes a member of our great team carrying a batch of milk towards me. The southern window frames the chickens free ranging, Sprouts kids, skipping by full of energy and brimming with questions, and workshop participants, smiling and listening intently on the lawn or in the garden.

Sometimes, one 18-hour, roller-coaster spring day interweaves the tone and feelings of all four seasons. I wake up exhilarated, capable and powerful. I can do this, I think, even if three more babies are born before the weekend. The exhaustion of birthing is almost done and the does are all healthy. Milking has a smooth cadence as my girls are giving in excess of a gallon per doe per day already. I am in the cheese house by 9:45 a.m., contentedly ladling curds and wrapping our standing cheese orders. As I work, the real farmer in me makes the bittersweet resolution to move the next set of bucklings off the farm even faster. And I reflect on the MontVivant because the bloomy pyramids have been terrific so far and are aging beautifully. I'm also planning a side-by-side comparison of two new cultures I've been trying out to push the flavor profile further.

And that's just a morning. In the afternoon, I'll take the Sprouts to see the spotted, twin lambs just born on the farm. Then I'll have only two hours to prepare a drop-dead farm dinner for Blue Hill at Stone Barns' chef Adam Kaye. I can count on the garden to save me with pea shoots, arugula, broccoli rabe, mint, radishes and spinach. And deep in such a spring day, I already sense in front of us summer's steady pace and plenty, the rush to the mixed feelings of fall and the final contemplative cocoon of insular winter.

I may have started on this dream without a master plan but every part of it now comes neatly together in a closed loop. Unlike monoculture, our animals and crops are diversified and interdependent, thriving and never wasting. Maybe farming just one crop or raising one animal is simpler but I can't imagine it. And even though our farm programs evolved sequentially and somewhat independently, they too now feed one another richly, driving the farm forward. A vision that I could not name when I started now seems obvious to me: the beauty of the interwoven threads is central to my satisfaction and the dynamic, on-going growth of Rainbeau Ridge.

In each circling year, I've seen the farm strengthen with these relationships and interconnections. I may not have my own children to work the farm but the family of helping hands has certainly expanded. However, the burgeoning demand for our children's programs, our cheese, and our accessible agricultural workshops and events also poses unresolved questions about the future for me. We're close to the operating capacity of our land, our herd, our classroom and cheese house space, and I am reaching my own personal operating capacity.

Here is the thorny paradox: how do I pursue every lead, every idea and every opportunity that increasingly come my way and still live the dream? On one hand, there is indeed leverage in larger scale and I am still driven towards the affirmation of a financially sustainable business that also fulfills my personal need for growth and challenge. On the other hand, the physical and time demands are already taxing. Sometimes when I catch sight of my grey hair in the mirror, I pause. Should I scale back instead to be able to stop and smell the strawberries? In addition, there are others living in my world now; a community I am bound to and feel responsible for.

Maybe to grow the business, I will have to compromise by moving out of the goat barn and the day-to-day into the broader platform of expanded distribution, franchising or curriculum development. I will need to find that point of balance that gives me accolades and accomplishment while also preserving what I love: foraging for dinner in the garden, nurturing my animals and transforming the gift of their milk into cheese.

Just like in sleeping dreams, the farm has grown according to its own logic. Living the dream requires negotiating the inevitable harsh

realities that are inseparable from the romance of farming. I'm counting on my gut once again as I near what I sense is a turning point, or at least a fork in the road. As I navigate my next step, I encourage you to find your own One Step towards sustainable living.

No matter which step I take, there's no doubt what drives me: bucketfuls of milk, rainbows after thunderstorms, crowing roosters, translucent squash blossoms, bounding kids and aqua-blue eggs. With everything I know now, I'd do it all again to have nature in my life this way.

The dream will continue to unfold, the path will inevitably meander and the destination will remain unknown. If suddenly tomorrow I was forced to scale down for whatever reason, I'd beg to keep a pair of goats, just a pair of does, as Rainbeau Ridge began.

JUST DO IT? BUT NOT ALONE

MAYBE WITH FAITH AND JEWEL and their kids I could have managed solo but without my husband Mark and my sister Karen, I never could have built out the farm. My two greatest supporters in all that farming entails have been vital to the enterprise. Without the high bar that Mark sets with his own example, I might not have found the confidence to even start. Without Karen's gift of implementation and in-the-trenches problem-solving, I might have missed many ingenious homespun solutions. The buck may stop with me on the farm but Mark and Karen help me shoulder it on very level.

MARK

At the same time Mark was winding down from his banking career, he positioned himself to use his access and resources in philanthropies concerned with three missions: education, the environment and health care. On the broad scale we discovered a commonality of purpose and complimentary roles: he was thinking globally and I continued to act locally. In recent years he has gone on to found Mission Point Capital that invests in renewable energy and green technologies.

Sometimes our parallel paths make us like ships passing in the night. This year during my quiet time on the farm, he was in Africa. The same challenge I feel to my strength and my friendships can be challenges for Mark and me. Nevertheless, while it is nearly self-sustaining now, the farm was launched with Mark's resources. He is the first to proudly

introduce me as a farmer, to send articles about the farm on to friends or to give the guided tour. The cow he named Destiny was his fiftieth birthday gift and the first sheep born on the farm, Lucca, arrived on his birthday party day. He isn't above delivering a cheese order on his way to work or spending a morning at the farmers market talking up the cheese with authority. He relishes our produce and is my Number One cheese eater. I know he gets it; he remains my partner and best friend.

MARK'S TAKE

Working the farm is strenuous but we're grounded enough to weather it, I think, in part because we've been together since Lisa was fifteen and I was sixteen. It has certainly changed our lives and although we're often off in different directions, we find a way to come together and rebalance. Our longevity as a couple helps us endure the stress and allows for more

compromises. Lisa and I respect each others' commitments. Everything we've done is as a partnership and a family, and every venture is a joint venture. Even if I'm only a modest part of the farm, we are collectively engaged in it. I brag about Lisa and the farm with pride.

We're both living the advice we give our children: pursue what you're passionate about, good at and interested in gaining expertise in. We're both making a contribution, building AIDS hospitals in South Africa, building a clean energy company and building Rainbeau Ridge.

The fact is nobody ever changed the world working forty hours a week. To make deep commitment to anything in which you want to excel, it has to consume you. You can't turn it on and off. I love that Lisa is totally absorbed in what she does and gets so much intellectual, emotional, even spiritual reward from it. Spending a day with her at a farmers market reminded me about her dedication. Nobody can sell her cheese like she can; her first-hand knowledge and her passion for quality come along with each piece.

The farm is a small business and like any small business, the owner is on 24/7. Lisa is not comfortable leaving the responsibility to someone else. Farming on this scale is challenging anywhere and all the more so in Westchester, one of the most expensive counties in America. Taxes are very high, labor costs are at a premium, and feed, supplies and veterinary care are more expensive here too. What most people don't realize, though, is that the regulatory pressure and additional cost of government scrutiny are very tough on a small farm. Given those costs, the initial capital investments required and the time it takes to build a brand and a reputation, it's wonderful that she's nearing the break-even point at year six. To me, the farm is almost a community trust because each of the farm programs is contributing to and influencing our community. But sustainable also means financially sustainable and, while she is most passionate about cheesemaking, her commitment and willingness to diversify make the farm work.

That said, we didn't envision the farm as a business. There was no business plan, much as I think having one is a good idea. We both want to protect open rural space and we love the look, smell and activity of a farm. But Lisa had a big idea and just dove into suburban farming with courage. She sensed a trend back when we were still in Japan. I recall her predicting that a time would come when people would want to know where their food came from. There is no punch line when we say that Rainbeau Ridge all started with two goats.

Lisa and Karen's amazing and complementary relationship has also moved the farm forward. They each think the other is the best person in the world and they each have the self-awareness to respect each others' strengths. Lisa is the visionary and the idea generator but Karen is the Execution Queen, down on her knees in the weeds, figuratively and occasionally literally.

Lisa has also become more meticulous herself over time, both financially and in her husbandry. She's an excellent farmer and has developed tremendous expertise—she's all but a vet herself. She keeps all the records, medicates, tattoos, performs the gross and the difficult, regardless of whether it's January 20 in the teeth of a blizzard or March 14 in the midst of a three-day downpour: she does it all with a prodigious work ethic and with a commitment to making the farm a success for everyone. I love her and I love those qualities.

KAREN

And what would I do without my genius sister, Karen? Because she is ten years younger than me, we hardly had a chance to know one another growing up. I was out of our parents' house by the time Kar was seven and I started dating Mark when she was five. Luckily, after she graduated from college, we gravitated toward one another and our connection has grown ever since. Although we consider ourselves very different from each other, everyone notices that we often finish each other's sentences.

After a successful career in financial services, Kar has chosen to stay home with her children. Little by little she has taken on a greater role at the farm, first as an organizer and leader of our children's program, Sprouts, then as our photographer and manager of the public perception of the farm via our website. She is so capable that I rely on her ability to figure out just about anything. She's quick to show you her manicured nails; Kar is not a farmer or a grower. "I don't get my hands dirty," she says, but I've caught her cuddling the newborn kids, picking up chicks and even shoveling worms.

I may have built the platform at Rainbeau Ridge but Kar sees the potential; she can move us forward. I never have to rescue Kar but sometimes she rescues me by balancing my starker, less tactful style. When I want to be brutally honest (BH), she counters with, "You can't say that…" I like to be right; while she knows how to say less and let go of a mistake or a loss. Karen rolls her eyes when I start spouting ideas. She knows how to talk me down from my indignation and temper me. "When are you going to do that? Wait, you're going to be away? How will that work?"

Kar has always understood the level of service, quality, care and integrity I strive for. She always has my proxy and like the does, Tina (Turner) and Faith (Hill), the two doelings born to Carly just after the first Faith died, we seek each other out constantly.

KAREN'S TAKE

My involvement with Rainbeau Ridge started when Lisa and I brought together a loose group of interested mothers a few years ago to explore starting a children's program at the farm. Finally after endless meetings, I just said, "Fine. We're starting in January and if we can make it in the dead of winter, we'll expand." That's my style; I'm more about getting things done and less about ideas. I'm the one who pushes to wrap it up, let it go, get it done and move on.

When I left the business world in 2001, Lisa reminded me that no one would give me a bonus or pat me on the back as a stay-at-home mom. In so many ways working with Lisa has made up for that. It's been so rewarding. Her praise, her intense appreciation and our mutual admiration society are irreplaceable. To have grown so close after growing up so distant is wonderful too. She's my best friend. I'm her resident generalist: our official photographer, the Website manager, program administrator, special events manager and marketing department.

And it's a good thing because I stink at farming. I can't grow a vegetable. I know my limits but both our skills and personalities are complementary. I'm quiet when Lisa is crabby. I'm skeptical and cynical when she's off and running with enthusiasm. She has the ideas and I help see them through. I'm the peacemaker and she's BH. I'm a tempering force. But we are also very much alike. Lisa and I are both workaholics, both time-sensitive and deadline-driven people. We regularly check in with one another on our response to a situation and we maintain a high standard for ourselves and others. We're perfectionists. Snacks for a Sprouts session can't just be pretzels. In fact, we might even reject homemade mommy-goat cookies and keep pushing past midnight for the just-right solution. That can sometimes be frustrating for us and hard to be around for others.

An important role I play is to remind Lisa to trust her gut. She has amazing instincts with farming and she's rarely wrong. She's only sorry when she goes against her innate intuition. When a doe is near kidding, Lisa will wonder whether she should induce the doe or go in to see if the labor is progressing, or if the kid is in a position that will make it more difficult for the delivery. She looks around and asks out loud, "Should I go in? Should I give her some more power punch? Should I call Dan?" After letting the questions echo away in the barn for a moment, I'd respond as if I had the most enlightened idea, "What does your gut tell you?" Sure enough, Lisa's gut is almost always right and she's saved more kids and does—and positively affected more people's lives—than she'll ever admit. 🐐

ACKNOWLEDGMENTS

The decision to start up Rainbeau Ridge and the guts to follow through wouldn't have happened without the inspiration and enduring hard work of fellow farmers and cheesemakers. Generous in spirit and there with advice when needed, we'd like to thank: Annie Farrell; the team at Stone Barns Center for Food & Agriculture, in particular, Dan Barber, David Barber, Laureen Barber, Irene Hamburger; Nancy & Jerry Kohlberg; Shirley & George Bianco; Dina Brewster; Jesse & Betsy Fink; Dot Hempler; Lynn Fleming; Carol Bunnell; members of The New York State Cheese Guild; Ricki Carroll; Sylvianne & Yves Johanneau; and members of The Bedford Farmers Club, The NY Unit of the Herb Society and Rusticus Garden Club.

Ever grateful for their assistance and moral support, we want to acknowledge the volunteers and friends who helped shape the farm and its story. We thank Diane Ferris, Melinda Walsh, Patrice & Rob Martin, Donna Marino & Maggie, Aimee Whitman & Georgia, Harriet Zeller, Nina Freedman, Cara Rosenbaum, Nick Gutfreund, Jaime Chapin, and Whitney Brown. We are indebted to all the farm's customers—CAP members, families of Roots, Buds and Sprouts and cooking class participants.

Ever present friends Michael Kaufman & Barbara Alpert, Vanessa Diebold, Kristen Lochrie, Melinda Papp, Linda Dishner, Lauren & Gary Cohen, Barbara Posner, Joan Zimmett, Debbie Chapman and Samantha Sichel were there when we needed them, even before we knew we needed them, nourishing us, never hesitating to promote us or make connections for us.

Early believers include a host of retailers, chefs and restaurateurs who had faith in our product and gave us the courage to push forward. A huge thank you to Ken Skovron, Joe DiMauro, Mona Spilo, Erica Sanford, chefs Adam Kaye (more salt!), Phil McGrath, and Jeff Raider.

The farm's success depended upon spreading the word throughout the broader community—the *Bedford Record Review*, *The Journal News*, *The New York Times*, *The Valley Table*, and *Westchester Magazine* were instrumental in helping us in our outreach.

Dr. Dan Hochman and Dr. Elizabeth Kilgallon brought the wisdom of their veterinary profession to balance with practical farming con-siderations, prevailing when we needed them most.

The farm would not function if not for the efforts of our collaborative team of Kevin Ferris, Ron Brooks, Isaac Jahns, Martha Hoffman and Kelly Hatton. We are grateful for the wonderful teachers of our Roots, Buds and Sprouts programs in Susan Shaw, Nancy Joffe and Lynn Schofield and for the culinary classes under Nicki Sizemore's leadership.

As is the case with the farm, it took more than any one individual to make this book a reality. Each with something unique to contribute, motivated by the end goal, the three of us navigated our way forward and collaborated in good faith. We are each grateful for the patience, persistence, critical eye and trust of each other.

The astute comments, keen insights and brutal honesty from our writing, designing, publishing and advertising friends were invaluable. We want to acknowledge Russell Reich, Tim Hawley, Renee Cho, Maura Rosenthal, Robert Berenson, Kelly Hatton, Mary Beth Roche and David Gernert.

The forbearance and cheerleading of our respective families were indispensable. Knowing that they were there for us, even if we weren't, we want to express our heartfelt thanks and love to Mark, Bari & Dan Schwartz, Bruce, Jeremy & Michael Sabath, Sandy Horwitz, Laura Foster, Enid & Stan Schwartz, Margie & Marty Sabath, Alice Hausman, Ben & Hannah Tressler, Amy, Scott, Melissa, Robbie & Jake Horwitz, Elizabeth, Wallace, Sam & Andrew Schwartz.

Finally, there would be no farm without the goats, chickens and even the soil that, in return for our caring and tending, give back and teach us so much, season after season. ❧

RESOURCES

Every cheesemaker or farmer is a resource but use this list to jump-start your own research. We've listed supportive organizations, informational sites and supply distributors.

CHEESE

For supplies...

Dairy Connection at www.dairyconnection.com

New England Cheesemaking Supply Company at www.cheesemaking.com

Formaticum at www.formaticum.com

Servidoryl at www.servidoryl.com

For events and professional support...

American Cheese Society at www.cheesesociety.org, the national organization.

New York Cheese Guild at www.nyfarmcheese.org

Other state organizations, such as Wisconsin Center for Dairy Research at www.cdr.wisc.edu and Vermont Institute for Artisan Cheese at www.uvm.edu/viac

To connect with cheesemakers...

CreamLine: The Home Dairy News at www.smalldairy.com

Culture at www.cheesemag.com

GOATS AND OTHER LIVESTOCK

For supplies...

Agway stores at www.agway.com

Caprine at www.caprinesupply.com

Hoegger at www.hoeggergoatsupply.com

For information and professional support…

Alliance Pastorale at www.alliancepastorale.fr

American Dairy Goat Association at www.adga.org

American Livestock Breeds Conservancy at www.albc-usa.org

Fias Co Farm at www.fiascofarm.com

CHICKENS & EGGS

For chicks and supplies…

Murray McMurray Hatchery at www.mcmurrayhatchery.com

For information…

www.backyardchickens.com

BEES

For supplies and information…

Better Bee at www.betterbee.com

MAPLE SYRUP

For tools and information…

www.sugarbushsupplies.com

GROWING

To connect with farmers, home gardeners, heirloom seeds, tools, CSAs and farmers markets…

www.gardens.com

Gardeners Supply at www.gardeners.com

Johnny's Seeds at www.johnnyseeds.com

Local Harvest at www.localharvest.org

State-by-state searching for pick-your-own operations at www.pickyourown.org

Seeds Savers Exchange at www.seedsavers.org

For events, publications and professional support…

Cornell Cooperative Extensions at www.cce.cornell.edu (and other similar regional extensions)

The Herb Society of America at www.herbsociety.org

National Agricultural Library at www.nal.usda.gov

National Garden Association at www.garden.org.

Northeast Organic Farming Association at www.nofa.org: (and other similar regional organizations, such as Pennsylvania Association for Sustainable Agriculture at www.pasafarming.org)

For gardening with children, including curriculum...

www.kidsgardening.org

4-H at www.4-h.org

The Edible Schoolyard at www.edibleschoolyard.org

SUSTAINABLE EATING

Blue Ocean at www.blueocean.com

Chef's Collaborative at www.chefscollaborative.org

Eat Wild at www.eatwild.com

Slow Food USA at www.slowfoodusa.org

Sustainable Table at www.sustainabletable.org

KEY RETAILERS WE MENTION

The Bedford Gourmet, 914-234-9409: Mona Spilo's gourmet shop is packed with great food.

Cowgirl Creamery, www.cowgirlcreamery.com: Sue Conley and Peggy Smith sell artisan cheeses from more than 200 American and European cheesemakers.

Darien Cheese and Fine Foods, www.dariencheese.com: Ken Skovron is an exceptionally knowledgeable cheesemonger.

Mt. Kisco Seafood and The Fish Cellar restaurant, www.fishcellar.com: Joe DiMauro is not only an ethical fishmonger but also a tireless supporter of local products.

CHEF CONTRIBUTORS

Michael Anthony: Formerly at Blue Hill at Stone Barns, now at Gramercy Tavern, a Manhattan landmark. www.gramercytavern.com

John Ash: Influential California chef at the Vintners Inn of Ferrraro-Carano vineyards in Sonoma, CA. www.chefjohnash.com,vintnersinn.com

Lauren Braun Costello: Chef, food stylist and author of Notes on Cooking (RCR Creative Press, 2009). www.thecompetentcook.com

Dan Barber: Executive chef and co-owner of Blue Hill at Stone Barns, Pocantico Hills, NY. www.bluehillfarm.com

Randall Dodge: Baker who makes biscotti and seasonal savory tarts with our cheese. www.redbarn-bakery.com

Johnny Holzworth: Chef of the stylish Dressing Room restaurant, Westport CT. www.dressingroomhomegrown.com

Adam Kaye: VP Culinary Affairs at Blue Hill at Stone Barns, Pocantico Hills, NY. www.bluehillfarm.com

Reza Khorshidi: Chef-partner of Rebecca Kirhoffer in the namesake Rebeccas in nearby Greenwich, CT. www.rebeccas.moonfruit.com

Dan Leader: Founder of the legendary Bread Alone, Boiceville, NY, one of the first widely distributed artisanal bread bakeries. www.breadalone.com

Phil McGrath: Our early supporter and the community-minded chef-owner of the esteemed Iron Horse Grill, Pleasantville, NY. www.ironhorsegrill.com

Jeff Raider: Long-time Westchester chef and now executive chef for The Grand Tier at Lincoln Center in Manhattan. www.lincolncenter.org

Theo Roe: Chef of American Bounty, regionally-focused restaurant at The Culinary Institute of America, Hyde Park, NY. www.ciachef.edu/restaurants/bounty/

Nicki Sizemore: Chef, food writer and manager of the In Lisa's Kitchen series at Rainbeau Ridge.

Brendan Walsh: Chef-owner of Brendans at the Elms in Ridgefield, CT. www.brendansattheelms.com

Robert Weland: Chef of the elegant Poste Brasserie in Washington, DC. www.postebrasserie.com

Michael Williams: Chef and co-owner of the popular local café and traiteur, The Perennial Chef, Bedford Hills, NY. www.theperennialchef.com

SEASONAL INDEX OF RECIPES

INDEX OF RECIPES BY CHEESE TYPE

All other recipes utilize only fresh goat cheese or goat milk.

INDEX OF RECIPES BY KEY INGREDIENT

If I ever go looking for my heart's desire again,
I won't look any further than my own backyard . . .

—Dorothy, *The Wizard of Oz*, movie script by Noel Langley, Florence Ryerson and
Edgar Allen Woolf, based on the book by L. Frank Baum, 1939